National Par
Bucket Journal

ISBN: 978-1-63933-047-8
Publish date July 1, 2021
Publisher: My Bucket Journals, LLC
PO Box 310, Hutto TX 78634

Disclaimer
The information in this book is based on the author's opinion, knowledge and experience. The publisher and the author will not be held liable for the use or misuse of the information contained herein.

Disclosure
This book may contain affiliate links. If you click through an affiliate link to a third-party website and make a purchase, the author may receive a small commission.

2021 National Parks Bucket Journal

The 2021 National Parks Bucket Journal is one part trip planner, one part bucket list, and one part journal. Use it as a place to plan your journey and record your memories. When you're done, you'll have a journal to look back at the National Park adventures you had with family and friends.

National Parks have been a part of our heritage since the first park was dedicated by President Ulysses S. Grant in 1872. There are currently 63 parks designated as "National Parks" covering 52.2 million acres of beautiful land to enjoy. In addition, there are even more preserves, reserves, memorials, and monuments. *Use the NPS App to find all the parks to explore (see page 128 for details)*

This completely updated 2021 journal is organized into 7 regions (Pacific NW & Alaska, Western, Southwest, Midwest, Rocky Mountain, North & Mid Atlantic, and Southeast) and then alphabetically by state. This grouping allows you to choose an area where you live, or will soon visit, and see the National Parks that are around you without flipping through the whole book.

Each of the 63 National Parks has its own 2-page spread with plenty of room to plan, discover, and document your trip.

- ❑ Use the left side page to learn more about the park and plan the attractions you want to see. We've given you a few ideas, but each park has more to discover.
- ❑ This page also has the address, phone number, and GPS coordinates for each park.
- ❑ Our fun, "by the numbers" section gives you an idea about the number of visitors each year (as of 2019), the number of entrances, and the number of visitor centers for each park.
- ❑ The second page gives you journal prompts to document your memories of the trip. Record who you were with, how you got there, and the views and vistas you loved the most.
- ❑ There is a dedicated space on this page to add a park stamp. Get creative as you personalize your journal.
- ❑ Is there a new park since publication? We've included blank pages for 5 more parks, so your journal won't become outdated.

Throughout the journal ,you'll find additional information to make your trip a success. We want you to experience every inch of America's National Parks!

Be sure to check our online interactive map, you'll get coordinates for each park and visitor center, plus a link to the National Park website for each park. Find it at https://cutt.ly/national-park-map

TABLE OF CONTENTS

Pacific NW & Alaska Region... 5
- ❑ Denali National Park... 6
- ❑ Gates of the Arctic National Park... 8
- ❑ Glacier Bay National Park... 10
- ❑ Katmai National Park and Preserve... 12
- ❑ Kenai Fjords National Park... 14
- ❑ Kobuk Valley National Park... 16
- ❑ Lake Clark National Park... 18
- ❑ Wrangell | St. Elias National Park and Preserve... 20
- ❑ Crater Lake National Park... 22
- ❑ Mount Rainier National Park... 24
- ❑ North Cascades National Park... 26
- ❑ Olympic National Park... 28

Western Region 31
- ❑ National Park of American Samoa... 32
- ❑ Grand Canyon National Park... 34
- ❑ Petrified Forest National Park... 36
- ❑ Saguaro National Park... 38
- ❑ Channel Islands National Park... 40
- ❑ Death Valley National Park... 42
- ❑ Joshua Tree National Park... 44
- ❑ Kings Canyon National Park... 46
- ❑ Lassen Volcanic National Park... 48
- ❑ Pinnacles National Park... 50
- ❑ Redwood National Park... 52
- ❑ Sequoia National Park... 54
- ❑ Yosemite National Park... 56
- ❑ Haleakala National Park... 58
- ❑ Hawaii Volcanoes National Park... 60
- ❑ Great Basin National Park... 62

Southwest Region 65
- ❑ Hot Springs National Park... 66
- ❑ Carlsbad Caverns National Park... 68
- ❑ White Sands National Park...70
- ❑ Big Bend National Park... 72
- ❑ Guadalupe Mountains National Park... 74

Midwest Region 77
- ❑ Indiana Dunes National Park... 78
- ❑ Isle Royale National Park... 80
- ❑ Voyageurs National Park... 82
- ❑ Gateway Arch National Park... 84
- ❑ Cuyahoga Valley National Park... 86

Rocky Mountain Region 89
- ❑ Black Canyon of the Gunnison National Park... 90
- ❑ Great Sand Dunes National Park and Preserve... 92
- ❑ Mesa Verde National Park... 94
- ❑ Rocky Mountain National Park... 96
- ❑ Glacier National Park... 98
- ❑ Theodore Roosevelt National Park... 100
- ❑ Badlands National Park... 102
- ❑ Wind Cave National Park... 104
- ❑ Arches National Park... 106
- ❑ Bryce Canyon National Park... 108
- ❑ Canyonlands National Park... 110
- ❑ Capitol Reef National Park... 112
- ❑ Zion National Park... 114
- ❑ Grand Teton National Park... 116
- ❑ Yellowstone National Park... 118

North & Mid Atlantic Regions 120
- ❑ Other parks in the NE Region... 121
- ❑ Acadia National Park... 122
- ❑ Shenandoah National Park... 124
- ❑ New River Gorge National Park ... 126

Southeast Region 129
- ❑ Biscayne National Park... 130
- ❑ Dry Tortugas National Park... 132
- ❑ Everglades National Park... 134
- ❑ Mammoth Cave National Park... 136
- ❑ Congaree National Park... 138
- ❑ Great Smoky Mountains National Park... 140
- ❑ Virgin Islands National Park... 142

Add New Parks
- ❑ ______________________144
- ❑ ______________________146
- ❑ ______________________148
- ❑ ______________________150
- ❑ ______________________152

Planning your trip? Be sure to visit our interactive map. Find it here: https://cutt.ly/national-park-map

PACIFIC NORTHWEST & ALASKA REGION

- Alaska
- Oregon
- Washington

DENALI NATIONAL PARK & PRESERVE

State: Alaska   Date Est: February 26, 1917

Explore the Park Virtually: https://www.nps.gov/dena/index.htm

Address:
Mile 237, Highway 3.
Denali AK 99755

Open all year _____Y_____N

dates___________________

- ☐ Phone (907) 683-9532
- ☐ Park Hours ____________
- ☐ Entrance $ ____________
- ☐ Timed Entrance _________
- ☐ Camp Sites $ ___________
- ☐ RV Sites $ ____________
- ☐ Refund policy

____

____

By the Numbers:

- ☐ 600,000+ visitors per year
- ☐ 6,075,106 acres
- ☐ Lat. 63.73089, Long. -148.91716
- ☐ 1 park entrance
- ☐ 5 visitor centers
- ☐ Highest elevation 20,310 ft.
- ☐ Lowest elevation 240 ft.

Attractions to Experience:

- ☐ Denali's Mountain Vista ☐
- ☐ Polychrome Overlook ☐
- ☐ Eielson Visitor Center ☐
- ☐ Reflection Pond ☐
- ☐ Wonder Lake ☐
- ☐ The Denali Bus Depot ☐
- ☐ Historic Headquarters ☐
- ☐ Savage River ☐
- ☐ Stargazing & Aurora Borealis ☐

Notes

____

____

____

____

____

____

____

____

____

____

____

Plan Your Trip:

- ☐ Staying at: ______________

  ____

  ____
- ☐ Phone ________________
- ☐ Reservations? ____Y ____N

  for dates ________________
- ☐ Check in time ___________
- ☐ Check out time __________
- ☐ Dog friendly _____Y ____N
- ☐ Max RV length ___________
- ☐ Dump Station location

  ____

  ____
- ☐ Distance from home

  miles: ________________

  hours: ________________

JOURNAL THE ADVENTURE

Why I went:

Dates I was in the park:

Where I stayed:

Who I went with:

How I got there: (circle all that apply)

Weather Experienced

Rate the Park

1 2 3 4 5

Will I go again?

Yes Maybe No

Memorable sights and experiences:

Something funny:

Something surprising:

Something disappointing:

One thing I want to remember about this trip:

GATES OF THE ARCTIC NATIONAL PARK

State: Alaska — Date Est: December 2, 1980

Explore the Park Virtually: https://www.nps.gov/gaar/index.htm

Address:
Morris Thompson Cultural & Visitors Center
101 Dunkel St,
Fairbanks, AK 99701

Open all year _____Y_____N

dates___________________

- ❑ Phone (907) 459-3730
- ❑ Park Hours ____________
- ❑ Entrance $ ____________
- ❑ Timed Entrance _________
- ❑ Camp Sites $ __________
- ❑ RV Sites $ ____________
- ❑ Refund policy

____

____

By the Numbers:

- ❑ 10,000+ visitors per year
- ❑ 7.5+ million acres
- ❑ Lat. 64.846, Long. -147.71272
- ❑ 4 park entrance
- ❑ 4 visitor centers
- ❑ Highest elevation 8,276 ft.
- ❑ Lowest elevation 280 ft.

Attractions to Experience:

- ❑ Arrigetch Peaks glacier
- ❑ Float a wild & scenic river
- ❑ Backpack the Brooks Range
- ❑ Anaktuvuk Pass VC
- ❑ Arctic Interagency VC
- ❑ Bettles Ranger Station
- ❑ Fairbanks AK Public Lands info center
- ❑
- ❑
- ❑
- ❑
- ❑
- ❑
- ❑
- ❑
- ❑
- ❑

Notes

____

____

____

____

____

____

____

____

____

____

____

Plan Your Trip:

- ❑ Staying at: ______________

  ____

  ____
- ❑ Phone ________________
- ❑ Reservations? ____Y ____N

  for dates ______________
- ❑ Check in time __________
- ❑ Check out time _________
- ❑ Dog friendly _____Y ____N
- ❑ Max RV length __________
- ❑ Dump Station location

  ____

  ____
- ❑ Distance from home

  miles: ______________

  hours: ______________

JOURNAL THE ADVENTURE

Why I went:

Dates I was in the park:

Where I stayed:

Who I went with:

How I got there: (circle all that apply)

Weather Experienced

Rate the Park

1 2 3 4 5

Will I go again?

Yes Maybe No

Memorable sights and experiences:

Something funny:

Something surprising:

Something disappointing:

One thing I want to remember about this trip:

GLACIER BAY NATIONAL PARK

State: Alaska **Date Est: December 2, 1980**

Explore the Park Virtually: https://www.nps.gov/glba/index.htm

Address:
1 Park Rd, Gustavus,
Hoonah-Angoon, AK 99826

Open all year _____Y_____N

dates___________________

- ❑ Phone (907) 697-2230
- ❑ Park Hours ____________
- ❑ Entrance $ ____________
- ❑ Timed Entrance _________
- ❑ Camp Sites $ ___________
- ❑ RV Sites $ _____________
- ❑ Refund policy

____

____

By the Numbers:

- ❑ 672,000+ visitors per year
- ❑ 3.3 million acres
- ❑ Lat. 58.6658, Long. -136.90021
- ❑ 4 park entrances
- ❑ 3 visitor centers
- ❑ Highest elevation 15,300 ft.
- ❑ Lowest elevation 0 ft.

Attractions to Experience:

- ❑ Glacier Bay VC
- ❑ Xunaa Shuka Hit Tribal House
- ❑ Historic Glacier Bay Lodge
- ❑ Bartlett Cove public dock
- ❑ Sea Otter Canoe
- ❑ Dry Bay
- ❑ Raven & Eagle Totem Pole
- ❑ Grand Pacific Glacier
- ❑ Beardslee Islands
- ❑ Forest Loop Trail walk
- ❑ Take a bird tour
- ❑ Glacier Bay Boat Tour
- ❑
- ❑
- ❑
- ❑
- ❑
- ❑

Notes

____

____

____

____

____

____

____

____

____

____

____

Plan Your Trip:

- ❑ Staying at: _______________

  ____

  ____
- ❑ Phone _________________
- ❑ Reservations? ____Y ____N

  for dates _______________
- ❑ Check in time ___________
- ❑ Check out time __________
- ❑ Dog friendly _____Y ____N
- ❑ Max RV length ___________
- ❑ Dump Station location

  ____

  ____
- ❑ Distance from home

  miles: _________________

  hours: _________________

JOURNAL THE ADVENTURE

Why I went:

Dates I was in the park:

Where I stayed:

Who I went with:

How I got there: (circle all that apply)

Weather Experienced

Rate the Park

1 2 3 4 5

Will I go again?

Yes Maybe No

Memorable sights and experiences:

Something funny:

Something surprising:

Something disappointing:

One thing I want to remember about this trip:

KATMAI NATIONAL PARK & PRESERVE

State: Alaska　　Date Est: December 2, 1980

Explore the Park Virtually: https://www.nps.gov/katm/index.htm

Address:
1 King Salmon Airport Rd,
King Salmon County,
Bristol Bay, AK 99613

Open all year _____Y_____N

dates___________________

- ❑ Phone (907) 246-3305
- ❑ Park Hours ____________
- ❑ Entrance $ ____________
- ❑ Timed Entrance _________
- ❑ Camp Sites $ __________
- ❑ RV Sites $ ____________
- ❑ Refund policy

____

____

By the Numbers:

- ❑ 84,000+ visitors per year
- ❑ 4.7 million+ acres
- ❑ Lat. 63.728443, Long. -148.886572
- ❑ 2 park entrances
- ❑ 3 visitor centers
- ❑ Highest elevation 7,606 ft.
- ❑ Lowest elevation 0 ft.

Attractions to Experience:

- ❑ Brooks Camp VC
- ❑ King Salmon VC
- ❑ Robert Griggs VC
- ❑ Fure's Cabin
- ❑ Brooks River Archaeological District
- ❑ Amalik Bay NH Landmark
- ❑ Hike to Dumpling Overlook
- ❑ Valley of Ten Thousand Smokes guided tour
- ❑ Explore Katmai by air
- ❑
- ❑
- ❑
- ❑
- ❑
- ❑

Plan Your Trip:

- ❑ Staying at: ____________

  ____

  ____
- ❑ Phone ______________
- ❑ Reservations? ____Y ____N

  for dates ____________
- ❑ Check in time __________
- ❑ Check out time __________
- ❑ Dog friendly _____Y ____N
- ❑ Max RV length __________
- ❑ Dump Station location

  ____

  ____
- ❑ Distance from home

  miles: ______________

  hours: ______________

Notes

____

____

____

____

____

____

____

____

____

____

____

JOURNAL THE ADVENTURE

Why I went:

Dates I was in the park:

Where I stayed:

Who I went with:

How I got there: (circle all that apply)

Weather Experienced

Rate the Park

1 2 3 4 5

Will I go again?

Yes Maybe No

Memorable sights and experiences:

Something funny:

Something surprising:

Something disappointing:

One thing I want to remember about this trip:

KENAI FJORDS NATIONAL PARK

State: Alaska   Date Est: December 2, 1980

Explore the Park Virtually: https://www.nps.gov/kefj/index.htm

Address:
Visitor Center
1212 4th Ave,
Seward, AK 99664

Open all year _____Y_____N

dates__________________

- ❑ Phone (907) 422-0500
- ❑ Park Hours ____________
- ❑ Entrance $ ____________
- ❑ Timed Entrance _________
- ❑ Camp Sites $ __________
- ❑ RV Sites $ ____________
- ❑ Refund policy

____

____

By the Numbers:

- ❑ 356,000+ visitors per year
- ❑ 669,000+ acres
- ❑ Lat. 59.84867, Long. -150.18788
- ❑ 1 park entrance
- ❑ 2 visitor centers
- ❑ Highest elevation 6,450 ft.
- ❑ Lowest elevation 0 ft.

Attractions to Experience:

- ❑ Kenai Fjords boat tour
- ❑ Flightseeing Harding Icefield
- ❑ Exit Glacier Nature Center
- ❑ Hike the Lower Trails
- ❑ Hike the Harding Icefield Trail
- ❑ Fishing in Seward
- ❑ Junior Ranger program
- ❑
- ❑

- ❑
- ❑
- ❑
- ❑
- ❑
- ❑
- ❑
- ❑
- ❑

Notes

____

____

____

____

____

____

____

____

____

____

____

Plan Your Trip:

- ❑ Staying at: ______________

  ____

  ____

- ❑ Phone ______________
- ❑ Reservations? ____Y ____N

  for dates ______________

- ❑ Check in time __________
- ❑ Check out time __________
- ❑ Dog friendly _____Y ____N
- ❑ Max RV length __________
- ❑ Dump Station location

  ____

  ____

- ❑ Distance from home

  miles: ______________

  hours: ______________

JOURNAL THE ADVENTURE

Why I went:

Dates I was in the park:

Where I stayed:

Who I went with:

How I got there: (circle all that apply)

Weather Experienced

Rate the Park

1 2 3 4 5

Will I go again?

Yes Maybe No

Memorable sights and experiences:

Something funny:

Something surprising:

Something disappointing:

One thing I want to remember about this trip:

KOBUK VALLEY NATIONAL PARK

State: Alaska Date Est: December 2, 1980

Explore the Park Virtually: https://www.nps.gov/kova/index.htm

Address:
Visitor Center
171 Third Ave,
Kotzebue, AK 99752

Open all year _____Y_____N

dates__________________

- ❑ Phone (907) 442-3890
- ❑ Park Hours ____________
- ❑ Entrance $ ____________
- ❑ Timed Entrance _________
- ❑ Camp Sites $ __________
- ❑ RV Sites $ ____________
- ❑ Refund policy

____

____

By the Numbers:

- ❑ 15,000+ visitors per year
- ❑ 1.75 million+ acres
- ❑ Lat. 66.89258, Long. -162.60508
- ❑ 1 park entrance
- ❑ 1 visitor center
- ❑ Highest elevation 4,629 ft.
- ❑ Lowest elevation 40 ft.

Attractions to Experience:

- ❑ NW Arctic Heritage Center
- ❑ Back Country Camping
- ❑ Float the Kobuk River
- ❑ Great Kobuk Sand Dunes
- ❑ Onion Portage Archaeological district
- ❑ Snap a pic of Jade Mountains
- ❑
- ❑
- ❑
- ❑
- ❑
- ❑
- ❑
- ❑
- ❑
- ❑

Plan Your Trip:

- ❑ Staying at: ____________

  ____

  ____
- ❑ Phone ______________
- ❑ Reservations? ____Y ____N

  for dates ______________
- ❑ Check in time __________
- ❑ Check out time _________
- ❑ Dog friendly _____Y ____N
- ❑ Max RV length __________
- ❑ Dump Station location

  ____

  ____
- ❑ Distance from home

  miles: ______________

  hours: ______________

Notes

____

____

____

____

____

____

____

____

____

____

____

JOURNAL THE ADVENTURE

Why I went:

Dates I was in the park:

Where I stayed:

Who I went with:

How I got there: (circle all that apply)

Weather Experienced

Rate the Park

1 2 3 4 5

Will I go again?

Yes Maybe No

Memorable sights and experiences:

Something funny:

Something surprising:

Something disappointing:

One thing I want to remember about this trip:

LAKE CLARK NATIONAL PARK

State: Alaska

Date Est: December 2, 1980

Explore the Park Virtually: https://www.nps.gov/lacl/index.htm

Address:
Visitor Center
1 Park Place,
Port Alsworth, AK 99653

Open all year _____Y_____N

dates___________________

- ❑ Phone (907) 781-2218
- ❑ Park Hours ____________
- ❑ Entrance $ ____________
- ❑ Timed Entrance _________
- ❑ Camp Sites $ ___________
- ❑ RV Sites $ _____________
- ❑ Refund policy

____

____

By the Numbers:

- ❑ 17,000+ visitors per year
- ❑ 2.6 million+ acres
- ❑ Lat. 60.41271, Long. -154.32349
- ❑ 1 park entrance
- ❑ 1 visitor center
- ❑ Highest elevation 20,310 ft.
- ❑ Lowest elevation 240 ft.

Attractions to Experience:

- ❑ Port Alsworth Visitor Center
- ❑ Richard Proenneke Cabin Tour
- ❑ Kayak at Twin Lakes
- ❑ Denison Sawmill exhibit
- ❑ Spend a night in Priest Rock cabin
- ❑ Camp at Kontrashibura Lake
- ❑ Hike Tanalian Mountain
- ❑ Fish on Lake Clark
- ❑ Fly fishing at Tanalian Falls
- ❑ Sport fishing on Upper Twin Lake
- ❑
- ❑
- ❑
- ❑
- ❑

Plan Your Trip:

- ❑ Staying at: _______________

  ____

  ____
- ❑ Phone ________________
- ❑ Reservations? ____Y ____N

  for dates _______________
- ❑ Check in time ___________
- ❑ Check out time __________
- ❑ Dog friendly _____Y ____N
- ❑ Max RV length ___________
- ❑ Dump Station location

  ____

  ____
- ❑ Distance from home

  miles: ________________

  hours: ________________

Notes

____

____

____

____

____

____

____

____

____

____

____

JOURNAL THE ADVENTURE

Why I went:

Dates I was in the park:

Where I stayed:

Who I went with:

How I got there: (circle all that apply)

Weather Experienced

Rate the Park

1 2 3 4 5

Will I go again?

Yes Maybe No

Memorable sights and experiences:

Something funny:

Something surprising:

Something disappointing:

One thing I want to remember about this trip:

WRANGELL-ST ELIAS NATIONAL PARK & PRESERVE

State: Alaska   Date Est: December 2, 1980

Explore the Park Virtually: https://www.nps.gov/wrst/index.htm

Address:
Visitor Center
Mile 106.8 Richardson Hwy
Copper Center, AK 99573

Open all year _____Y_____N

dates___________________

- ❑ Phone (907) 822-5234
- ❑ Park Hours ____________
- ❑ Entrance $ ____________
- ❑ Timed Entrance ________
- ❑ Camp Sites $ __________
- ❑ RV Sites $ ____________
- ❑ Refund policy

____

____

By the Numbers:

- ❑ 74,000+ visitors per year
- ❑ 13.2 million+ acres
- ❑ Lat. 61.71044,
  Long. -142.98568
- ❑ 2 park entrances
- ❑ 5 visitor centers
- ❑ Highest elevation 18,008 ft.
- ❑ Lowest elevation 1,150 ft.

Attractions to Experience:

- ❑ Kennecott Mines
- ❑ Root Glacier
- ❑ Yakutat Coastal Area
- ❑ McCarthy Road Audio Tour
- ❑ Nabesna Rd Audio Tour
- ❑ Kennecott Glacier Virtual Tour
- ❑ See the park film – Crown of the Continent
- ❑ Go Flightseeing to ghost towns
- ❑ View the park webcams
- ❑ Boreal Forest Trail Tour
- ❑
- ❑
- ❑
- ❑
- ❑

Plan Your Trip:

- ❑ Staying at: ______________

  ____

  ____
- ❑ Phone _______________
- ❑ Reservations? ____Y ____N

  for dates _______________
- ❑ Check in time __________
- ❑ Check out time __________
- ❑ Dog friendly _____Y ____N
- ❑ Max RV length __________
- ❑ Dump Station location

  ____

  ____
- ❑ Distance from home

  miles: _______________

  hours: _______________

Notes

____

____

____

____

____

____

____

____

____

____

____

JOURNAL THE ADVENTURE

Why I went:

Dates I was in the park:

Where I stayed:

Who I went with:

How I got there: (circle all that apply)

Weather Experienced

Rate the Park

1 2 3 4 5

Will I go again?

Yes Maybe No

Memorable sights and experiences:

Something funny:

Something surprising:

Something disappointing:

One thing I want to remember about this trip:

CRATER LAKE NATIONAL PARK

State: Oregon

Date Est: May 22, 1902

Explore the Park Virtually: https://www.nps.gov/crla/index.htm

Address:
Rim Village Visitor Center
Rim Dr,
Crater Lake, OR 97604

Open all year _____Y_____N

dates____________________

- ❑ Phone (541) 594-3000
- ❑ Park Hours ____________
- ❑ Entrance $ ____________
- ❑ Timed Entrance ________
- ❑ Camp Sites $ __________
- ❑ RV Sites $ ____________
- ❑ Refund policy

____

____

By the Numbers:

- ❑ 700,000+ visitors per year
- ❑ 183,000+ acres
- ❑ Lat. 42.91138,
  Long. -122.14346
- ❑ 3 park entrances
- ❑ 2 visitor centers
- ❑ Highest elevation 8,929 ft.
- ❑ Lowest elevation 3,990 ft.

Attractions to Experience:

- ❑ Rim Visitor Center
- ❑ Steel Visitor Center
- ❑ Take the Scenic Rim Drive
- ❑ Snowshoeing
- ❑ Biking
- ❑ Phantom Ship Overlook
- ❑ See the Pumice Desert
- ❑ Sinnott Memorial Overlook
- ❑ Crater Lake Lodge
- ❑
- ❑
- ❑
- ❑
- ❑
- ❑
- ❑
- ❑
- ❑

Notes

____

____

____

____

____

____

____

____

____

____

____

Plan Your Trip:

- ❑ Staying at: ______________

  ____

  ____

- ❑ Phone ________________
- ❑ Reservations? ____Y ____N

  for dates ________________

- ❑ Check in time ___________
- ❑ Check out time __________
- ❑ Dog friendly _____Y ____N
- ❑ Max RV length ___________
- ❑ Dump Station location

  ____

  ____

- ❑ Distance from home

  miles: ________________

  hours: ________________

JOURNAL THE ADVENTURE

Why I went:

Dates I was in the park:

Where I stayed:

Who I went with:

How I got there: (circle all that apply)

Weather Experienced

Rate the Park

1 2 3 4 5

Will I go again?

Yes Maybe No

Memorable sights and experiences:

Something funny:

Something surprising:

Something disappointing:

One thing I want to remember about this trip:

MOUNT RAINIER NATIONAL PARK

State: Washington

Date Est: Mar 2, 1899

Explore the Park Virtually: https://www.nps.gov/mora/index.htm

Address:
White River Wilderness VC
70002 WA-410,
Enumclaw, WA 98022

Open all year _____Y_____N

dates___________________

- ❑ Phone (360) 569-2211
- ❑ Park Hours _____________
- ❑ Entrance $ _____________
- ❑ Timed Entrance _________
- ❑ Camp Sites $ ___________
- ❑ RV Sites $ _____________
- ❑ Refund policy

____

____

By the Numbers:

- ❑ 1.5 million+ visitors per year
- ❑ 236,000+ acres
- ❑ Lat. 46.87996, Long. -121.7269
- ❑ 4 park entrances
- ❑ 8 visitor centers
- ❑ Highest elevation 14,411 ft.
- ❑ Lowest elevation 1,600 ft.

Attractions to Experience:

- ❑ Longmire Area
- ❑ Paradise Area
- ❑ Ohanapecosh Area
- ❑ Sunrise & White River Area
- ❑ Carbon River Area
- ❑ Mowich Lake
- ❑ Kautz Creek Boardwalk tour
- ❑ National Park Inn at Longmire
- ❑ Twin Firs Loop Trail
- ❑ Silver Falls Loop trail
- ❑ Grove of the Patriarchs Trail
- ❑ Journey to Paradise guided tour
- ❑ Sunrise Geology Audio Tour
- ❑
- ❑
- ❑

Notes

____

____

____

____

____

____

____

____

____

____

____

Plan Your Trip:

- ❑ Staying at: _______________

  ____

  ____
- ❑ Phone _________________
- ❑ Reservations? ____Y ____N

  for dates ________________
- ❑ Check in time __________
- ❑ Check out time __________
- ❑ Dog friendly _____Y ____N
- ❑ Max RV length ___________
- ❑ Dump Station location

  ____

  ____
- ❑ Distance from home

  miles: _________________

  hours: _________________

JOURNAL THE ADVENTURE

Why I went:

Dates I was in the park:

Where I stayed:

Who I went with:

How I got there: (circle all that apply)

Weather Experienced

Rate the Park

1 2 3 4 5

Will I go again?

Yes Maybe No

Memorable sights and experiences:

Something funny:

Something surprising:

Something disappointing:

One thing I want to remember about this trip:

NORTH CASCADES NATIONAL PARK

State: Washington

Date Est: October 2, 1968

Explore the Park Virtually https://www.nps.gov/noca/index.htm

Address:
Visitor Center
Marblemount, WA 98267

Open all year _____Y_____N

dates___________________

- ❑ Phone (206) 386-4495
- ❑ Park Hours ____________
- ❑ Entrance $ ____________
- ❑ Timed Entrance _________
- ❑ Camp Sites $ ___________
- ❑ RV Sites $ ____________
- ❑ Refund policy

____

____

By the Numbers:

- ❑ 38,000+ visitors per year
- ❑ 504,000+ acres
- ❑ Lat. 48.66634, Long. -121.26677
- ❑ 5 park entrances
- ❑ 4 visitor centers
- ❑ Highest elevation 9,206 ft.
- ❑ Lowest elevation 605 ft.

Attractions to Experience:

- ❑ Longmire Area
- ❑ Paradise Area
- ❑ Ohanapecosh Area
- ❑ Sunrise & White River Area
- ❑ Carbon River Area
- ❑ Mowich Lake
- ❑ Kautz Creek Boardwalk tour
- ❑ National Park Inn at Longmire
- ❑ Twin Firs Loop Trail
- ❑ Silver Falls Loop trail
- ❑ Grove of the Patriarchs Trail
- ❑ Journey to Paradise guided tour
- ❑ Sunrise Geology Audio Tour
- ❑
- ❑
- ❑

Notes

____

____

____

____

____

____

____

____

____

____

____

Plan Your Trip:

- ❑ Staying at: ______________

  ____

  ____
- ❑ Phone ______________
- ❑ Reservations? ____Y ____N

  for dates ______________
- ❑ Check in time __________
- ❑ Check out time __________
- ❑ Dog friendly _____Y ____N
- ❑ Max RV length ___________
- ❑ Dump Station location

  ____

  ____
- ❑ Distance from home

  miles: ______________

  hours: ______________

JOURNAL THE ADVENTURE

Why I went:

Dates I was in the park:

Where I stayed:

Who I went with:

How I got there: (circle all that apply)

Weather Experienced

Rate the Park

1 2 3 4 5

Will I go again?

Yes Maybe No

Memorable sights and experiences:

Something funny:

Something surprising:

Something disappointing:

One thing I want to remember about this trip:

OLYMPIC NATIONAL PARK

State: Washington Date Est: January 29, 1938

Explore the Park Virtually https://www.nps.gov/olym/index.htm

Address:
Visitor Center
3002 Mt Angeles Rd,
Port Angeles, WA 98362

Open all year _____Y_____N

dates___________________

- ❑ Phone (360) 565-3130
- ❑ Park Hours ___________
- ❑ Entrance $ ___________
- ❑ Timed Entrance _________
- ❑ Camp Sites $ __________
- ❑ RV Sites $ ___________
- ❑ Refund policy

____

____

By the Numbers:

- ❑ 3.2 million+ visitors per year
- ❑ 992,000+ acres
- ❑ Lat. 47.8021, Long. -123.60435
- ❑ 8 park entrances
- ❑ 10 visitor centers
- ❑ Highest elevation 7,980 ft.
- ❑ Lowest elevation 0 ft.

Attractions to Experience:

- ❑ HOH Rainforest
- ❑ Elwha River Valley
- ❑ Sol Duc Valley
- ❑ Mora Coastal Area
- ❑ Quinault Rain Forest
- ❑ Ozette Triangle Hike
- ❑ Staircase Area
- ❑ Queets Valley
- ❑ Kalaloch Coastal Area
- ❑ Tidepooling on the coast
- ❑ Lake Crescent Lodge
- ❑ Lake Quinault Lodge
- ❑ Kalaloch Lodge
- ❑ Sol Duc Hot Springs
- ❑
- ❑
- ❑
- ❑

Plan Your Trip:

- ❑ Staying at: ______________

  ____

  ____
- ❑ Phone ________________
- ❑ Reservations? ____Y ____N

  for dates ______________
- ❑ Check in time __________
- ❑ Check out time __________
- ❑ Dog friendly _____Y ____N
- ❑ Max RV length __________
- ❑ Dump Station location

  ____

  ____
- ❑ Distance from home

  miles: ________________

  hours: ________________

Notes

____

____

____

____

____

____

____

____

____

____

____

JOURNAL THE ADVENTURE

Why I went:

Dates I was in the park:

Where I stayed:

Who I went with:

How I got there: (circle all that apply)

Weather Experienced

Rate the Park

1 2 3 4 5

Will I go again?

Yes Maybe No

Memorable sights and experiences:

Something funny:

Something surprising:

Something disappointing:

One thing I want to remember about this trip:

10 THINGS TO TAKE & DO ON YOUR NATIONAL PARK TRIP

National Parks are America's gems. While you're out in nature, exploring and enjoying them, be sure to take and do these 10 things designed to help you stay safe and enjoy your trip.

- Safety is important when you are out in nature. Bring a first aid kit and manual so you are able to handle small bumps and bruises with ease.
- National Parks are wild places and weather changes rapidly. Don't get caught out in the country without warm clothing and blankets.
- Take simple poncho's or rain gear on your trip. They pack lightly and are easy to tuck away. Don't let a surprise storm ruin your trip!
- Carry water bottles with you at all times.
- Learn to purify water and have the proper equipment on hand.
- Always stay on the hiking trails.
- Animal proof the food you leave in your car and in your packs.
- Beware of the signs of altitude sickness and learn how to prevent it.
- Be aware and prevent Lyme disease by taking preventive steps
- Protect yourself from sunburn with sunblock or sunscreen.

Learn more in the article https://mybucketjournals.com/blogs/news/10-things-to-take-on-a-national-park-trip

WESTERN REGION

- American Samoa
- Arizona
- California
- Hawaii
- Nevada

NATIONAL PARK of AMERICAN SAMOA

State: American Samoa — Date Est: October 31, 1988

Explore the Park Virtually: https://www.nps.gov/npsa/index.htm

Address:
Visitor Center
MHJ Bldg., 2nd Floor
Pago Pago, AS 96799

Open all year _____Y_____N

dates___________________

- ❑ Phone (684) 633-7082 x22
- ❑ Park Hours ____________
- ❑ Entrance $ ____________
- ❑ Timed Entrance ________
- ❑ Camp Sites $ __________
- ❑ RV Sites $ ____________
- ❑ Refund policy

____

____

By the Numbers:

- ❑ 60,000+ visitors per year
- ❑ 10,000+ acres
- ❑ Lat. 61.71044, Long. -142.98568
- ❑ 1 park entrance
- ❑ 1 visitor center
- ❑ Highest elevation 3,170 ft.
- ❑ Lowest elevation 0 ft.

Attractions to Experience:

- ❑ Saua Village
- ❑ Cape TapuTapu
- ❑ Snap a pic of Mt Alava
- ❑ Boat ride to Aunu'u Island
- ❑ Hike Lower Sa'uma Trail
- ❑ Hike historic WWII Blunts Point Trail
- ❑ Fruit Bat watching in the Rainforest

- ❑
- ❑
- ❑
- ❑
- ❑
- ❑
- ❑
- ❑
- ❑

Notes

____

____

____

____

____

____

____

____

____

____

____

Plan Your Trip:

- ❑ Staying at: ______________

  ____

  ____
- ❑ Phone ________________
- ❑ Reservations? ____Y ____N

  for dates ______________
- ❑ Check in time __________
- ❑ Check out time _________
- ❑ Dog friendly _____Y ____N
- ❑ Max RV length __________
- ❑ Dump Station location

  ____

  ____
- ❑ Distance from home

  miles: ________________

  hours: ________________

JOURNAL THE ADVENTURE

Why I went:

Dates I was in the park:

Where I stayed:

Who I went with:

How I got there: (circle all that apply)

Weather Experienced

Rate the Park

1 2 3 4 5

Will I go again?

Yes Maybe No

Memorable sights and experiences:

Something funny:

Something surprising:

Something disappointing:

One thing I want to remember about this trip:

GRAND CANYON NATIONAL PARK

State: Arizona

Date Est: February 26, 1919

Explore the Park Virtually: https://www.nps.gov/grca/index.htm

Address:
Visitor Center
S Entrance Rd,
Grand Canyon Village, AZ 86023

- ❑ Phone (928) 638-7888
- ❑ Park Hours ____________
- ❑ Entrance $ ____________
- ❑ Timed Entrance _________
- ❑ Camp Sites $ ___________
- ❑ RV Sites $ ____________
- ❑ Refund policy

____

____

Open all year _____Y_____N

dates__________________

By the Numbers:

- ❑ 5.9 million+ visitors per year
- ❑ 1.2 million+ acres
- ❑ Lat. 36.10692, Long. -112.11294
- ❑ 3 park entrances
- ❑ 2 visitor centers
- ❑ Highest elevation 3,170 ft.
- ❑ Lowest elevation 0 ft.

Attractions to Experience:

- ❑ Grand Canyon Geology Tour
- ❑ South Rim Tour
- ❑ Hike part of Bright Angel Trail (north rim)
- ❑ Mather Point to Yavapai Geology Museum (south rim)
- ❑ Bridle Path Trail (north rim)
- ❑ North Rim VC
- ❑ Grand Canyon VC

- ❑
- ❑
- ❑
- ❑
- ❑
- ❑
- ❑
- ❑
- ❑

Notes

____

____

____

____

____

____

____

____

____

____

____

Plan Your Trip:

- ❑ Staying at: ______________

  ____

  ____
- ❑ Phone ________________
- ❑ Reservations? ____Y ____N

  for dates ______________
- ❑ Check in time __________
- ❑ Check out time __________
- ❑ Dog friendly _____Y ____N
- ❑ Max RV length __________
- ❑ Dump Station location

  ____

  ____
- ❑ Distance from home

  miles: ________________

  hours: ________________

JOURNAL THE ADVENTURE

Why I went:

Dates I was in the park:

Where I stayed:

Who I went with:

How I got there: (circle all that apply)

Weather Experienced

Rate the Park

1 2 3 4 5

Will I go again?

Yes Maybe No

Memorable sights and experiences:

Something funny:

Something surprising:

Something disappointing:

One thing I want to remember about this trip:

PETRIFIED FOREST NATIONAL PARK

State: Arizona   Date Est: December 9, 1962

Explore the Park Virtually: https://www.nps.gov/pefo/index.htm

Address:
Visitor Center
1 Park Rd,
Petrified Forest National Park,
AZ 86028

Open all year _____Y_____N

dates___________________

- ❑ Phone (928) 524-6228
- ❑ Park Hours ____________
- ❑ Entrance $ ____________
- ❑ Timed Entrance _________
- ❑ Camp Sites $ ___________
- ❑ RV Sites $ _____________
- ❑ Refund policy

____

____

By the Numbers:

- ❑ 640,000+ visitors per year
- ❑ 221,000+ acres
- ❑ Lat. 35.06555, Long. -109.78166
- ❑ 2 park entrances
- ❑ 2 visitor centers
- ❑ Highest elevation 6,235 ft.
- ❑ Lowest elevation 5,300 ft.

Attractions to Experience:

- ❑ Rainbow Forest Museum
- ❑ Paleo Lab |Desert Forest VC
- ❑ Go Geocaching
- ❑ Self-guided tour | Giant Logs
- ❑ Walk Blue Mesa Trail
- ❑ Walk Crystal Forest Trail
- ❑ Walk Long Logs Trail
- ❑ Walk the Painted Desert Rim Trail

❑
❑
❑
❑
❑
❑
❑
❑
❑

Plan Your Trip:

- ❑ Staying at: ______________

____

____

- ❑ Phone ________________
- ❑ Reservations? ____Y ____N

for dates ________________

- ❑ Check in time ___________
- ❑ Check out time __________
- ❑ Dog friendly _____Y ____N
- ❑ Max RV length ___________
- ❑ Dump Station location

____

____

- ❑ Distance from home

miles: _________________

hours: _________________

Notes

____

____

____

____

____

____

____

____

____

____

____

JOURNAL THE ADVENTURE

Why I went:

Dates I was in the park:

Where I stayed:

Who I went with:

How I got there: (circle all that apply)

Weather Experienced

Rate the Park

1 2 3 4 5

Will I go again?

Yes Maybe No

Memorable sights and experiences:

Something funny:

Something surprising:

Something disappointing:

One thing I want to remember about this trip:

SAGUARO NATIONAL PARK

State: Arizona

Date Est: October 14, 1994

Explore the Park Virtually: https://www.nps.gov/sagu/index.htm

Address:
Red Hills Visitor Center
2700 N Kinney Rd,
Tucson, AZ 85743

Open all year _____Y_____N

dates___________________

- ❑ Phone (520) 733-5153
- ❑ Park Hours ____________
- ❑ Entrance $ ____________
- ❑ Timed Entrance _________
- ❑ Camp Sites $ ___________
- ❑ RV Sites $ ____________
- ❑ Refund policy

____

____

By the Numbers:

- ❑ 1 million+ visitors per year
- ❑ 91,000+ acres
- ❑ Lat. 32.25441, Long. -111.19732
- ❑ 6 park entrances
- ❑ 2 visitor centers
- ❑ Highest elevation 4,687 ft.
- ❑ Lowest elevation 2,180 ft.

Attractions to Experience:

- ❑ West District – Red Mills VC
- ❑ East District – Rincon Mt VC
- ❑ Hike at Mica View Picnic area
- ❑ Take the Bajada Loop Drive
- ❑ See petroglyphs from destinations along Signal Hill trails
- ❑ Stargazing
- ❑ Take a guided tour

- ❑
- ❑
- ❑
- ❑
- ❑
- ❑
- ❑
- ❑
- ❑

Plan Your Trip:

- ❑ Staying at: ______________

  ____

  ____

- ❑ Phone ________________
- ❑ Reservations? ____Y ____N

  for dates ________________

- ❑ Check in time __________
- ❑ Check out time __________
- ❑ Dog friendly _____Y ____N
- ❑ Max RV length __________
- ❑ Dump Station location

  ____

  ____

- ❑ Distance from home

  miles: _________________

  hours: _________________

Notes

____

____

____

____

____

____

____

____

____

____

____

JOURNAL THE ADVENTURE

Why I went:

Dates I was in the park:

Where I stayed:

Who I went with:

How I got there: (circle all that apply)

Weather Experienced

Rate the Park

1 2 3 4 5

Will I go again?

Yes Maybe No

Memorable sights and experiences:

Something funny:

Something surprising:

Something disappointing:

One thing I want to remember about this trip:

CHANNEL ISLANDS NATIONAL PARK

State: California

Date Est: March 5, 1980

Explore the Park Virtually: https://www.nps.gov/chis/index.htm

Address:
RJ Lagomarsino Visitor Center
1901 Spinnaker Dr,
Ventrua, CA 93001

Open all year _____Y_____N

dates____________________

- ❑ Phone (805) 658-5730
- ❑ Park Hours ____________
- ❑ Entrance $ ____________
- ❑ Timed Entrance _________
- ❑ Camp Sites $ __________
- ❑ RV Sites $ ____________
- ❑ Refund policy

____

____

By the Numbers:

- ❑ 400,000+ visitors per year
- ❑ 249,000+ acres
- ❑ Lat. 34.00693, Long. -119.77853
- ❑ 5 park entrances
- ❑ 7 visitor centers
- ❑ Highest elevation 2,429 ft.
- ❑ Lowest elevation 0 ft.

Attractions to Experience:

- ❑ Anacapa Island tour
- ❑ San Miguel Island tour
- ❑ Santa Barbara Island tour
- ❑ Santa Cruz Island tour
- ❑ Santa Rosa Island tour
- ❑ Arch Rock
- ❑ Channel Islands Light House
- ❑ Stargazing
- ❑ Take a guided tour
- ❑ Scorpion Ranch VC
- ❑ Prisoner's Harbor kayaking
- ❑
- ❑
- ❑
- ❑
- ❑
- ❑
- ❑

Plan Your Trip:

- ❑ Staying at: ______________

  ____

  ____

- ❑ Phone ________________
- ❑ Reservations? ____Y ____N

  for dates ______________

- ❑ Check in time __________
- ❑ Check out time _________
- ❑ Dog friendly _____Y ____N
- ❑ Max RV length __________
- ❑ Dump Station location

  ____

  ____

- ❑ Distance from home

  miles: ______________

  hours: ______________

Notes

____

____

____

____

____

____

____

____

____

____

____

JOURNAL THE ADVENTURE

Why I went:

Dates I was in the park:

Where I stayed:

Who I went with:

How I got there: (circle all that apply)

Weather Experienced

Rate the Park

1 2 3 4 5

Will I go again?

Yes Maybe No

Memorable sights and experiences:

Something funny:

Something surprising:

Something disappointing:

One thing I want to remember about this trip:

DEATH VALLEY NATIONAL PARK

State: California   Date Est: October 31, 1994

Explore the Park Virtually: https://www.nps.gov/deva/index.htm

Address:
Visitor Center
CA-190,
Death Valley, CA 92328

Open all year _____Y_____N

dates___________________

- ❑ Phone (760) 786-3200
- ❑ Park Hours ____________
- ❑ Entrance $ ____________
- ❑ Timed Entrance _________
- ❑ Camp Sites $ ___________
- ❑ RV Sites $ ____________
- ❑ Refund policy

____

____

By the Numbers:

- ❑ 1.7 million+ visitors per year
- ❑ 3.4 million+ acres
- ❑ Lat. 36.46175, Long. -116.86661
- ❑ 2 park entrances
- ❑ 1 visitor center
- ❑ Highest elevation 11,043 ft.
- ❑ Lowest elevation -282 ft.

Attractions to Experience:

- ❑ Badwater Basin
- ❑ Artists Palette
- ❑ Mesquite Flat Sand Dunes
- ❑ Devils Hole
- ❑ Ubehebe Crater
- ❑ Zabriskie Point
- ❑ Dante's View
- ❑ Stargazing
- ❑ Harmony Borax Works tour
- ❑ Furnace Creek VC
- ❑ Star Wars Film location tour
- ❑
- ❑
- ❑
- ❑
- ❑
- ❑
- ❑

Plan Your Trip:

- ❑ Staying at: ______________

  ____

  ____

- ❑ Phone ________________
- ❑ Reservations? ____Y ____N

  for dates ________________

- ❑ Check in time __________
- ❑ Check out time __________
- ❑ Dog friendly _____Y ____N
- ❑ Max RV length __________
- ❑ Dump Station location

  ____

  ____

- ❑ Distance from home

  miles: ________________

  hours: ________________

Notes

____

____

____

____

____

____

____

____

____

____

____

JOURNAL THE ADVENTURE

Why I went:

Dates I was in the park:

Where I stayed:

Who I went with:

How I got there: (circle all that apply)

Weather Experienced

Rate the Park

1 2 3 4 5

Will I go again?

Yes Maybe No

Memorable sights and experiences:

Something funny:

Something surprising:

Something disappointing:

One thing I want to remember about this trip:

JOSHUA TREE NATIONAL PARK

State: California   Date Est: October 31, 1994

Explore the Park Virtually: https://www.nps.gov/jotr/index.htm

Address:
Visitor Center
74485 National Park Drive
Twentynine Palms, CA 92277

Open all year _____Y_____N

dates___________________

- ❑ Phone (760) 367-5500
- ❑ Park Hours ____________
- ❑ Entrance $ ____________
- ❑ Timed Entrance _________
- ❑ Camp Sites $ __________
- ❑ RV Sites $ ____________
- ❑ Refund policy

____

____

By the Numbers:

- ❑ 2.9 million+ visitors per year
- ❑ 795,000+ acres
- ❑ Lat. 34.12873, Long. -116.03766
- ❑ 4 park entrances
- ❑ 4 visitor centers
- ❑ Highest elevation 5,816 ft.
- ❑ Lowest elevation 934 ft.

Attractions to Experience:

- ❑ Cholla Cactus Garden
- ❑ Cap Rock
- ❑ Skull Rock
- ❑ Lost Horse Mine
- ❑ Fortynine Palms Oasis
- ❑ Drive Park Boulevard
- ❑ Go Bouldering
- ❑ Stargazing at Cap Rock
- ❑ Birding & photography
- ❑
- ❑
- ❑
- ❑
- ❑
- ❑
- ❑
- ❑
- ❑

Notes

____

____

____

____

____

____

____

____

____

____

____

Plan Your Trip:

- ❑ Staying at: ______________

  ____

  ____
- ❑ Phone ________________
- ❑ Reservations? ____Y ____N

  for dates _______________
- ❑ Check in time __________
- ❑ Check out time __________
- ❑ Dog friendly _____Y ____N
- ❑ Max RV length __________
- ❑ Dump Station location

  ____

  ____
- ❑ Distance from home

  miles: _________________

  hours: _________________

JOURNAL THE ADVENTURE

Why I went:

Dates I was in the park:

Where I stayed:

Who I went with:

How I got there: (circle all that apply)

Weather Experienced

Rate the Park

1 2 3 4 5

Will I go again?

Yes Maybe No

Memorable sights and experiences:

Something funny:

Something surprising:

Something disappointing:

One thing I want to remember about this trip:

KINGS CANYON NATIONAL PARK

State: California

Date Est: March 4, 1940

Explore the Park Virtually: https://www.nps.gov/seki/index.htm

Address:
Kings Canyon Visitor Center
83918 CA-180,
Grant Grove Village, CA 93633

Open all year _____Y_____N

dates___________________

- ❑ Phone (559) 565-3341
- ❑ Park Hours _____________
- ❑ Entrance $ _____________
- ❑ Timed Entrance _________
- ❑ Camp Sites $ ____________
- ❑ RV Sites $ ______________
- ❑ Refund policy

____

____

By the Numbers:

- ❑ 600,000+ visitors per year
- ❑ 461,000+ acres
- ❑ Lat. 36.73999, Long. -118.96337
- ❑ 2 park entrances
- ❑ 2 visitor centers
- ❑ Highest elevation 14,494 ft.
- ❑ Lowest elevation 1,370 ft.

Attractions to Experience:

- ❑ Cedar Grove VC
- ❑ Panoramic Point overlook
- ❑ Visit Redwood Canyon
- ❑ Grant Grove Village
- ❑ Zumwalt Meadow
- ❑ John Muir Lodge
- ❑ Cedar Grove Lodge
- ❑ General Grant tree
- ❑ Kings Canyon Scenic By-way

- ❑
- ❑
- ❑
- ❑
- ❑
- ❑
- ❑
- ❑
- ❑

Notes

____

____

____

____

____

____

____

____

____

____

____

Plan Your Trip:

- ❑ Staying at: _______________

  ____

  ____

- ❑ Phone ___________________
- ❑ Reservations? ____Y ____N

  for dates _________________

- ❑ Check in time ___________
- ❑ Check out time ___________
- ❑ Dog friendly _____Y ____N
- ❑ Max RV length ___________
- ❑ Dump Station location

  ____

  ____

- ❑ Distance from home

  miles: ___________________

  hours: ___________________

JOURNAL THE ADVENTURE

Why I went:

Dates I was in the park:

Where I stayed:

Who I went with:

How I got there: (circle all that apply)

Weather Experienced

Rate the Park

1 2 3 4 5

Will I go again?

Yes Maybe No

Memorable sights and experiences:

One thing I want to remember about this trip:

Something funny:

Something surprising:

Something disappointing:

LASSEN VOLCANIC NATIONAL PARK

State: California

Date Est: August 9, 1916

Explore the Park Virtually: https://www.nps.gov/lavo/index.htm

Address:
Kohm Yah-mah-nee Visitor Ctr
21820 Lassen Peak Hwy,
Mineral, CA 96063

Open all year _____Y_____N

dates___________________

- ❑ Phone (530) 595-4480
- ❑ Park Hours _____________
- ❑ Entrance $ _____________
- ❑ Timed Entrance _________
- ❑ Camp Sites $ ___________
- ❑ RV Sites $ _____________
- ❑ Refund policy

____

____

By the Numbers:

- ❑ 500,000+ visitors per year
- ❑ 106,000+ acres
- ❑ Lat. 40.43778,
  Long. -121.53384
- ❑ 5 park entrances
- ❑ 2 visitor centers
- ❑ Highest elevation 10,457 ft.
- ❑ Lowest elevation 5,275 ft.

Attractions to Experience:

- ❑ Drive Lassen Volcanic National Park Highway
- ❑ Visit Sulphur Works
- ❑ Walk the Devastated Trail
- ❑ Walk the Manzanita Lake Trail
- ❑ Kings Creek Falls Trail
- ❑ Bumpass Hell Trail
- ❑ Geocaching, Earthcaching
- ❑ Fishing and Boating

- ❑
- ❑
- ❑
- ❑
- ❑
- ❑
- ❑
- ❑
- ❑

Notes

____

____

____

____

____

____

____

____

____

____

____

Plan Your Trip:

- ❑ Staying at: _______________

  ____

  ____
- ❑ Phone _________________
- ❑ Reservations? ____Y ____N

  for dates _______________
- ❑ Check in time __________
- ❑ Check out time __________
- ❑ Dog friendly _____Y ____N
- ❑ Max RV length ___________
- ❑ Dump Station location

  ____

  ____
- ❑ Distance from home

  miles: _________________

  hours: _________________

JOURNAL THE ADVENTURE

Why I went:

Dates I was in the park:

Where I stayed:

Who I went with:

How I got there: (circle all that apply)

Weather Experienced

Rate the Park

1 2 3 4 5

Will I go again?

Yes Maybe No

Memorable sights and experiences:

One thing I want to remember about this trip:

Something funny:

Something surprising:

Something disappointing:

PINNACLES NATIONAL PARK

State: California — Date Est: January 10, 2013

Explore the Park Virtually: https://www.nps.gov/pinn/index.htm

Address:
Visitor Center
5000 CA-146,
Paicines, CA 95043

Open all year _____Y_____N

dates__________________

- ❑ Phone (831) 389-4485
- ❑ Park Hours ____________
- ❑ Entrance $ ____________
- ❑ Timed Entrance _________
- ❑ Camp Sites $ ___________
- ❑ RV Sites $ _____________
- ❑ Refund policy

____

____

By the Numbers:

- ❑ 177,000+ visitors per year
- ❑ 26,000+ acres
- ❑ Lat. 36.49372,
  Long. -121.14644
- ❑ 2 park entrances
- ❑ 3 visitor centers
- ❑ Highest elevation 3,304 ft.
- ❑ Lowest elevation 824 ft.

Attractions to Experience:

- ❑ Bear Gulch Reservoir
- ❑ Bear Gulch Nature Center
- ❑ Hike Prewett Point Trail
- ❑ Visit West Pinnacles VC
- ❑ Bear Gulch Cave
- ❑ Balconies Cave
- ❑ Hike Moses Spring to Rim Trail Loop
- ❑ Condor Gulch Overlook

❑
❑
❑
❑
❑
❑
❑
❑
❑

Notes

____

____

____

____

____

____

____

____

____

____

____

Plan Your Trip:

- ❑ Staying at: ______________

  ____

  ____
- ❑ Phone _________________
- ❑ Reservations? ____Y ____N

  for dates ________________
- ❑ Check in time __________
- ❑ Check out time __________
- ❑ Dog friendly _____Y ____N
- ❑ Max RV length ___________
- ❑ Dump Station location

  ____

  ____
- ❑ Distance from home

  miles: _________________

  hours: _________________

JOURNAL THE ADVENTURE

Why I went:

Dates I was in the park:

Where I stayed:

Who I went with:

How I got there: (circle all that apply)

Weather Experienced

Rate the Park

1 2 3 4 5

Will I go again?

Yes Maybe No

Memorable sights and experiences:

Something funny:

Something surprising:

Something disappointing:

One thing I want to remember about this trip:

REDWOOD NATIONAL PARK

State: California

Date Est: October 2, 1968

Explore the Park Virtually: https://www.nps.gov/redw/index.htm

Address:
Visitor Center
1111 2nd St,
Crescent City, CA 95531

Open all year _____Y_____N

dates___________________

- ❑ Phone (707) 464-6101
- ❑ Park Hours ____________
- ❑ Entrance $ ____________
- ❑ Timed Entrance ________
- ❑ Camp Sites $ ___________
- ❑ RV Sites $ ____________
- ❑ Refund policy

____

____

By the Numbers:

- ❑ 500,000+ visitors per year
- ❑ 131,000+ acres
- ❑ Lat. 41.21317, Long. -124.00462
- ❑ 4 park entrances
- ❑ 4 visitor centers
- ❑ Highest elevation 3,262 ft.
- ❑ Lowest elevation 0 ft.

Attractions to Experience:

- ❑ Simpson Reed Grove
- ❑ Stout Memorial Grove
- ❑ Yurok Loop Trail
- ❑ Klamath River Overlook
- ❑ Big Tree Wayside
- ❑ Trillium Falls Trail
- ❑ Redwood Creek Overlook
- ❑ Drive Howland Hill Road
- ❑ Drive the Bald Hills
- ❑ Drive Newton B Drury Scenic Parkway
- ❑
- ❑
- ❑
- ❑
- ❑
- ❑
- ❑

Plan Your Trip:

- ❑ Staying at: ______________

  ____

  ____
- ❑ Phone ________________
- ❑ Reservations? ____Y ____N

  for dates ______________
- ❑ Check in time __________
- ❑ Check out time _________
- ❑ Dog friendly _____Y ____N
- ❑ Max RV length __________
- ❑ Dump Station location

  ____

  ____
- ❑ Distance from home

  miles: ________________

  hours: ________________

Notes

____

____

____

____

____

____

____

____

____

____

____

JOURNAL THE ADVENTURE

Why I went:

Dates I was in the park:

Where I stayed:

Who I went with:

How I got there: (circle all that apply)

Weather Experienced

Rate the Park

1 2 3 4 5

Will I go again?

Yes Maybe No

Memorable sights and experiences:

Something funny:

Something surprising:

Something disappointing:

One thing I want to remember about this trip:

SEQUOIA NATIONAL PARK

State: California — Date Est: September 25, 1890

Explore the Park Virtually: https://www.nps.gov/seki/index.htm

Address:
Foothills Visitor Center
47050 Generals Hwy,
Three Rivers, CA 93271

Open all year _____Y_____N

dates___________________

- ❑ Phone (559) 565-3341
- ❑ Park Hours _____________
- ❑ Entrance $ _____________
- ❑ Timed Entrance _________
- ❑ Camp Sites $ ___________
- ❑ RV Sites $ _____________
- ❑ Refund policy

____

____

By the Numbers:

- ❑ 1.2 million+ visitors per year
- ❑ 404,000+ acres
- ❑ Lat. 36.49097, Long. -118.82533
- ❑ 4 park entrances
- ❑ 4 visitor centers
- ❑ Highest elevation 14,505 ft.
- ❑ Lowest elevation 1,360 ft.

Attractions to Experience:

- ❑ Giant Forest Museum
- ❑ Mineral King Ranger Station
- ❑ Crystal Cave
- ❑ General Sherman Tree
- ❑ Wolverton Meadow Loop
- ❑ Hospital Rock pictograph
- ❑ Moro Rock
- ❑ Drive through Tunnel Log
- ❑
- ❑
- ❑
- ❑
- ❑
- ❑
- ❑
- ❑
- ❑
- ❑

Notes

____

____

____

____

____

____

____

____

____

____

____

Plan Your Trip:

- ❑ Staying at: _______________

  ____

  ____

- ❑ Phone _______________
- ❑ Reservations? ____Y ____N

  for dates _______________

- ❑ Check in time __________
- ❑ Check out time __________
- ❑ Dog friendly _____Y ____N
- ❑ Max RV length __________
- ❑ Dump Station location

  ____

  ____

- ❑ Distance from home

  miles: _______________

  hours: _______________

JOURNAL THE ADVENTURE

Why I went:

Dates I was in the park:

Where I stayed:

Who I went with:

How I got there: (circle all that apply)

Weather Experienced

Rate the Park

1 2 3 4 5

Will I go again?

Yes Maybe No

Memorable sights and experiences:

Something funny:

Something surprising:

Something disappointing:

One thing I want to remember about this trip:

YOSEMITE NATIONAL PARK

State: California

Date Est: October 1, 1890

Explore the Park Virtually: https://www.nps.gov/yose/index.htm

Address:
Yosemite Valley VC
9035 Village Dr,
Yosemite Valley, CA 95389

Open all year _____Y_____N

dates____________________

- ❑ Phone (209) 372-0200
- ❑ Park Hours _____________
- ❑ Entrance $ _____________
- ❑ Timed Entrance _________
- ❑ Camp Sites $ ___________
- ❑ RV Sites $ _____________
- ❑ Refund policy

____

____

By the Numbers:

- ❑ 1.2 million+ visitors per year
- ❑ 404,000+ acres
- ❑ Lat. 37.74859, Long. -119.58741
- ❑ 5 park entrances
- ❑ 4 visitor centers
- ❑ Highest elevation 13,114 ft.
- ❑ Lowest elevation 2,105 ft.

Attractions to Experience:

- ❑ Bridalveil Fall
- ❑ Tunnel View
- ❑ Swinging Bridge Picnic Area
- ❑ Sentinel Bridge
- ❑ Yosemite Museum
- ❑ Mirror Lake
- ❑ Drive Glacier Point Road
- ❑ Drive Tioga Road
- ❑ Drive Hetch Hetchy Road
- ❑ See Wawona & Mariposa Groves
- ❑
- ❑
- ❑
- ❑
- ❑
- ❑
- ❑

Notes

____

____

____

____

____

____

____

____

____

____

____

Plan Your Trip:

- ❑ Staying at: _______________

  ____

  ____
- ❑ Phone _________________
- ❑ Reservations? ____Y ____N

  for dates _______________
- ❑ Check in time __________
- ❑ Check out time __________
- ❑ Dog friendly _____Y ____N
- ❑ Max RV length ___________
- ❑ Dump Station location

  ____

  ____
- ❑ Distance from home

  miles: _________________

  hours: _________________

JOURNAL THE ADVENTURE

Why I went:

Dates I was in the park:

Where I stayed:

Who I went with:

How I got there: (circle all that apply)

Weather Experienced

Rate the Park

1 2 3 4 5

Will I go again?

Yes Maybe No

Memorable sights and experiences:

Something funny:

Something surprising:

Something disappointing:

One thing I want to remember about this trip:

HALEAKALA NATIONAL PARK

State: Hawaii

Date Est: July 1, 1961

Explore the Park Virtually: https://www.nps.gov/hale/index.htm

Address:
Visitor Center
30000 Haleakala Hwy,
Kula, Maui, 96790

Open all year _____Y_____N

dates___________________

- ❑ Phone (808) 572-4400
- ❑ Park Hours ____________
- ❑ Entrance $ ____________
- ❑ Timed Entrance _________
- ❑ Camp Sites $ ___________
- ❑ RV Sites $ ____________
- ❑ Refund policy

____

____

By the Numbers:

- ❑ 900,000+ visitors per year
- ❑ 33,000+ acres
- ❑ Lat. 20.71508,
  Long. -156.24981
- ❑ 1 park entrance
- ❑ 3 visitor centers
- ❑ Highest elevation 10,023 ft.
- ❑ Lowest elevation 0 ft.

Attractions to Experience:

- ❑ Kīpahulu VC in the coastal district
- ❑ Haleakalā VC at the summit
- ❑ Headquarters VC
- ❑ Bamboo Forest / Pīpīwai trail
- ❑ Makahiku Falls overlook
- ❑ Hale Hālāwai
- ❑ Hike to Haleakalā's Crater
- ❑ Hike to Leleiwi Overlook
- ❑
- ❑
- ❑
- ❑
- ❑
- ❑
- ❑
- ❑
- ❑

Notes

____

____

____

____

____

____

____

____

____

____

____

Plan Your Trip:

- ❑ Staying at: ______________

  ____

  ____
- ❑ Phone ________________
- ❑ Reservations? ____Y ____N

  for dates ______________
- ❑ Check in time __________
- ❑ Check out time __________
- ❑ Dog friendly _____Y ____N
- ❑ Max RV length __________
- ❑ Dump Station location

  ____

  ____
- ❑ Distance from home

  miles: ________________

  hours: ________________

JOURNAL THE ADVENTURE

Why I went:

Dates I was in the park:

Where I stayed:

Who I went with:

How I got there: (circle all that apply)

Weather Experienced

Rate the Park

1 2 3 4 5

Will I go again?

Yes Maybe No

Memorable sights and experiences:

Something funny:

Something surprising:

Something disappointing:

One thing I want to remember about this trip:

HAWAII VOLCANOES NATIONAL PARK

State: Hawaii

Date Est: August 1, 1916

Explore the Park Virtually: https://www.nps.gov/havo/index.htm

Address:
Visitor Center
1 Crater Rim Dr,
Volcano, Hawaii, 96785

Open all year _____Y_____N

dates__________________

- ❑ Phone (808) 985-6000
- ❑ Park Hours ___________
- ❑ Entrance $ ___________
- ❑ Timed Entrance _________
- ❑ Camp Sites $ __________
- ❑ RV Sites $ ____________
- ❑ Refund policy

____

____

By the Numbers:

- ❑ 1.3 million+ visitors per year
- ❑ 325,000+ acres
- ❑ Lat. 19.42962, Long. -155.25713
- ❑ 3 park entrances
- ❑ 2 visitor centers
- ❑ Highest elevation 10,023 ft.
- ❑ Lowest elevation 0 ft.

Attractions to Experience:

- ❑ Crater Rim Drive Tour
- ❑ Explore Maunaulu lava flow
- ❑ Hike to Pu'uloa Petroglyphs
- ❑ Hike Ha'akulamanu (Sulphur Banks) Trail
- ❑ Day Hike- Nāhuku (Thurston Lava Tube)
- ❑ Day Hike – Kīpukapuaulu
- ❑ Explore the Kahuku Unit

❑
❑
❑
❑
❑
❑
❑
❑
❑

Notes

____

____

____

____

____

____

____

____

____

____

____

Plan Your Trip:

- ❑ Staying at: ______________

  ____

  ____
- ❑ Phone _______________
- ❑ Reservations? ____Y ____N

  for dates _______________
- ❑ Check in time __________
- ❑ Check out time __________
- ❑ Dog friendly _____Y ____N
- ❑ Max RV length __________
- ❑ Dump Station location

  ____

  ____
- ❑ Distance from home

  miles: _______________

  hours: _______________

JOURNAL THE ADVENTURE

Why I went:

Dates I was in the park:

Where I stayed:

Who I went with:

How I got there: (circle all that apply)

Weather Experienced

Rate the Park

1 2 3 4 5

Will I go again?

Yes Maybe No

Memorable sights and experiences:

Something funny:

Something surprising:

Something disappointing:

One thing I want to remember about this trip:

GREAT BASIN NATIONAL PARK

State: Nevada

Date Est: October 27, 1986

Explore the Park Virtually: https://www.nps.gov/grba/index.htm

Address:
Lehman Caves Visitor Center
5500 NV-488,
Baker, NV 89311

Open all year _____Y_____N

dates___________________

- ❑ Phone (775) 234-7331
- ❑ Park Hours ____________
- ❑ Entrance $ ____________
- ❑ Timed Entrance _________
- ❑ Camp Sites $ ___________
- ❑ RV Sites $ ____________
- ❑ Refund policy

____

____

By the Numbers:

- ❑ 131,000+ visitors per year
- ❑ 77,000+ acres
- ❑ Lat. 39.00558, Long. -114.21982
- ❑ 12 park entrances
- ❑ 2 visitor centers
- ❑ Highest elevation 13,060 ft.
- ❑ Lowest elevation 1,195 ft.

Attractions to Experience:

- ❑ Lehman Cave tours
- ❑ International Dark-Sky Park, try a Ranger led astronomy program
- ❑ See Bristlecone pines in Wheeler Peak Grove
- ❑ Drive the Wheeler Peak Scenic Trail
- ❑ Snap a pic at Mather Overlook

❑
❑
❑
❑
❑
❑
❑
❑
❑

Notes

____

____

____

____

____

____

____

____

____

____

____

Plan Your Trip:

- ❑ Staying at: ______________

  ____

  ____

- ❑ Phone ______________
- ❑ Reservations? ____Y ____N

  for dates ______________

- ❑ Check in time __________
- ❑ Check out time __________
- ❑ Dog friendly _____Y ____N
- ❑ Max RV length __________
- ❑ Dump Station location

  ____

  ____

- ❑ Distance from home

  miles: ________________

  hours: ________________

JOURNAL THE ADVENTURE

Why I went:

Dates I was in the park:

Where I stayed:

Who I went with:

How I got there: (circle all that apply)

Weather Experienced

Rate the Park

1 2 3 4 5

Will I go again?

Yes Maybe No

Memorable sights and experiences:

Something funny:

Something surprising:

Something disappointing:

One thing I want to remember about this trip:

NATIONAL PARK TRIVIA

1. What is the largest national park?

A Denali National Park

B Wrangell-St. Elias National Park

C Death Valley National Park

2. Which is the smallest national park?

A Cuyahoga Valley National Park

B Mesa Verde National Park

C Hot Springs National Park

3. Which park has the highest elevation?

A Grand Teton National Park

B Denali National Park

C Mount Rainier National Park

4. Which park has the lowest elevation?

A Death Valley National Park

B Biscayne National Park

C Everglades National Park

5. What park was designated the FIRST National Park? Bonus points if you can name the year!

A Sequoia National Park

B Mount Rainier National Park

C Yellowstone National Park

6. What is the NEWEST national park (as of December 2020)

A Pinnacles National Park

B New River Gorge National Park

C Congaree National Park

7. Which National Park is the home to the largest tree by volume?

A Sequoia National Park

B Joshua Tree National Park

C Redwood National Park

8. Most visited National Park

A Great Smokey Mountains National Park

B Yellowstone National Park

C Yosemite National Park

9. Which state contains the most National Parks?

A Utah

B California

C Alaska

10. Which is the least visited National Park?

A Dry Tortugas National Park

B Black Canyon of the Gunnison NP

C Isle Royal National Park

Answer Key: 1=B, 2= C, 3=B, 4=A, 5=C 1872, 6=B, 7=A, 8=A, 9=B, 10=C

SOUTHWEST REGION

- Arkansas
- New Mexico
- Texas

HOT SPRINGS NATIONAL PARK

State: Arkansas

Date Est: March 4, 1921

Explore the Park Virtually: https://www.nps.gov/hosp/index.htm

Address:
Fordyce Bathhouse
Visitor Center
369 Central Ave,
Hot Springs, AR 71901

Open all year _____Y_____N

dates___________________

- ❑ Phone (501) 620-6715
- ❑ Park Hours ____________
- ❑ Entrance $ ____________
- ❑ Timed Entrance _________
- ❑ Camp Sites $ ___________
- ❑ RV Sites $ _____________
- ❑ Refund policy

____

____

By the Numbers:

- ❑ 1.4 million+ visitors per year
- ❑ 5,500+ acres
- ❑ Lat. 34.51371, Long. -93.05345
- ❑ 6 park entrances
- ❑ 1 visitor center
- ❑ Highest elevation 1,405 ft.
- ❑ Lowest elevation 415 ft.

Attractions to Experience:

- ❑ Soak in the springs at Buckstaff or Quapaw Bathhouse
- ❑ Fill your water bottle from several fountain locations
- ❑ Hike Hot Springs Trail
- ❑ Snap a pic at the overlook on Goat Rock Trail
- ❑ Take a ranger led tour
- ❑ Snap a pic at Mountain Tower
- ❑ Take the cell phone tour of Bathhouse Row
- ❑
- ❑
- ❑
- ❑
- ❑
- ❑
- ❑

Notes

____

____

____

____

____

____

____

____

____

____

____

Plan Your Trip:

- ❑ Staying at: _______________

  ____

  ____

- ❑ Phone _______________
- ❑ Reservations? ____Y ____N

  for dates _______________

- ❑ Check in time __________
- ❑ Check out time __________
- ❑ Dog friendly _____Y ____N
- ❑ Max RV length ___________
- ❑ Dump Station location

  ____

  ____

- ❑ Distance from home

  miles: _______________

  hours: _______________

JOURNAL THE ADVENTURE

Why I went:

Dates I was in the park:

Where I stayed:

Who I went with:

How I got there: (circle all that apply)

Weather Experienced

Rate the Park

1 2 3 4 5

Will I go again?

Yes Maybe No

Memorable sights and experiences:

One thing I want to remember about this trip:

Something funny:

Something surprising:

Something disappointing:

CARLSBAD CAVERNS NATIONAL PARK

State: New Mexico

Date Est: May 14, 1930

Explore the Park Virtually: https://www.nps.gov/cave/index.htm

Address:
Visitor Center
727 Carlsbad Cavern Hwy,
Carlsbad, NM 88220

Open all year _____Y_____N

dates___________________

- ❑ Phone (575) 785-2232
- ❑ Park Hours ____________
- ❑ Entrance $ ____________
- ❑ Timed Entrance _________
- ❑ Camp Sites $ ___________
- ❑ RV Sites $ _____________
- ❑ Refund policy

____

____

By the Numbers:

- ❑ 440,000+ visitors per year
- ❑ 46,000+ acres
- ❑ Lat. 32.17546, Long. -104.44423
- ❑ 1 park entrance
- ❑ 1 visitor center
- ❑ Highest elevation 6,368 ft.
- ❑ Lowest elevation 3,596 ft.

Attractions to Experience:

- ❑ Explore Big Room Trail
- ❑ Experience Natural Entrance Trail (steep hike)
- ❑ Take on of 8 Ranger Guided tours
- ❑ Drive Walnut Canyon Desert Scenic Drive
- ❑ Experience the Chihuahuan Desert Nature Trail

❑
❑
❑
❑
❑
❑
❑
❑
❑

Notes

____

____

____

____

____

____

____

____

____

____

____

Plan Your Trip:

- ❑ Staying at: _______________

  ____

  ____

- ❑ Phone _______________
- ❑ Reservations? ____Y ____N

  for dates _______________

- ❑ Check in time __________
- ❑ Check out time __________
- ❑ Dog friendly _____Y ____N
- ❑ Max RV length __________
- ❑ Dump Station location

  ____

  ____

- ❑ Distance from home

  miles: _______________

  hours: _______________

JOURNAL THE ADVENTURE

Why I went:

Dates I was in the park:

Where I stayed:

Who I went with:

How I got there: (circle all that apply)

Weather Experienced

Rate the Park

1 2 3 4 5

Will I go again?

Yes Maybe No

Memorable sights and experiences:

Something funny:

Something surprising:

Something disappointing:

One thing I want to remember about this trip:

WHITE SANDS NATIONAL PARK

State: New Mexico   Date Est: December 20, 2019

Explore the Park Virtually: https://www.nps.gov/whsa/index.htm

Address:
Visitor Center
19955 US-70,
Alamogordo, NM 88310

Open all year _____Y_____N

dates___________________

- ❑ Phone (575) 479-6124
- ❑ Park Hours ____________
- ❑ Entrance $ ____________
- ❑ Timed Entrance _________
- ❑ Camp Sites $ ___________
- ❑ RV Sites $ _____________
- ❑ Refund policy

____

____

By the Numbers:

- ❑ 600,000+ visitors per year
- ❑ 146,000+ acres
- ❑ Lat. 32.77961,
  Long. -106.17245
- ❑ 1 park entrance
- ❑ 1 visitor center
- ❑ Highest elevation 4,235 ft.
- ❑ Lowest elevation 3,887 ft.

Attractions to Experience:

- ❑ Experience scenic Dunes Drive ❑
- ❑ Walk Interdune Boardwalk ❑
- ❑ Playa Trail ❑
- ❑ Dune Life Nature Trail ❑
- ❑ Alkali Flat Trail (strenuous) ❑
- ❑ Go sledding! ❑
- ❑ Ranger Tour – Sunset Stroll ❑
- ❑ Take a Full Moon Ranger Hike ❑
- ❑ Lake Lucero Tour ❑

Notes

____

____

____

____

____

____

____

____

____

____

____

Plan Your Trip:

- ❑ Staying at: ______________

  ____

  ____
- ❑ Phone ________________
- ❑ Reservations? ____Y ____N

  for dates _______________
- ❑ Check in time __________
- ❑ Check out time __________
- ❑ Dog friendly _____Y ____N
- ❑ Max RV length __________
- ❑ Dump Station location

  ____

  ____
- ❑ Distance from home

  miles: _________________

  hours: _________________

JOURNAL THE ADVENTURE

Why I went:

Dates I was in the park:

Where I stayed:

Who I went with:

How I got there: (circle all that apply)

Weather Experienced

Rate the Park

1 2 3 4 5

Will I go again?

Yes Maybe No

Memorable sights and experiences:

Something funny:

Something surprising:

Something disappointing:

One thing I want to remember about this trip:

BIG BEND NATIONAL PARK

State: Texas

Date Est: January 12, 1944

Explore the Park Virtually: https://www.nps.gov/bibe/index.htm

Address:
Panther Junction Visitor Center
310, Alsate Dr,
Big Bend National Park, TX
79834

Open all year _____Y_____N

dates___________________

- ❑ Phone (432) 477-2251
- ❑ Park Hours ____________
- ❑ Entrance $ ____________
- ❑ Timed Entrance _________
- ❑ Camp Sites $ ___________
- ❑ RV Sites $ ____________
- ❑ Refund policy

____

____

By the Numbers:

- ❑ 460,000+ visitors per year
- ❑ 801,000+ acres
- ❑ Lat. 29.32782, Long. -103.20592
- ❑ 3 park entrances
- ❑ 5 visitor centers
- ❑ Highest elevation 7,625 ft.
- ❑ Lowest elevation 1,715 ft.

Attractions to Experience:

- ❑ Ross Maxwell Scenic Drive ❑
- ❑ Chisos Mountains Lodge ❑
- ❑ Visit Castolon Historic District ❑
- ❑ Visit Fossil Discovery Exhibit ❑
- ❑ Walk the Window View Trail in the Chisos Mountains ❑ ❑
- ❑ Scenic Santa Elena Canyon ❑
- ❑ Take in a Night Sky Program in this Int'l Dark Sky Park ❑ ❑

Notes

____

____

____

____

____

____

____

____

____

____

____

Plan Your Trip:

- ❑ Staying at: ______________

  ____

  ____
- ❑ Phone _________________
- ❑ Reservations? ____Y ____N

  for dates _______________
- ❑ Check in time ___________
- ❑ Check out time __________
- ❑ Dog friendly _____Y ____N
- ❑ Max RV length __________
- ❑ Dump Station location

  ____

  ____
- ❑ Distance from home

  miles: _________________

  hours: _________________

JOURNAL THE ADVENTURE

Why I went:

Dates I was in the park:

Where I stayed:

Who I went with:

How I got there: (circle all that apply)

Weather Experienced

Rate the Park

1 2 3 4 5

Will I go again?

Yes Maybe No

Memorable sights and experiences:

Something funny:

Something surprising:

Something disappointing:

One thing I want to remember about this trip:

GUADALUPE MOUNTAINS NATIONAL PARK

State: Texas

Date Est: October 15, 1966

Explore the Park Virtually: https://www.nps.gov/gumo/index.htm

Address:
Pine Springs Visitor Center
400 Pine Canyon Dr,
Salt Flat, TX 79847

Open all year _____Y_____N

dates__________________

- ❑ Phone (915) 828-3251
- ❑ Park Hours ____________
- ❑ Entrance $ ____________
- ❑ Timed Entrance _________
- ❑ Camp Sites $ ___________
- ❑ RV Sites $ ____________
- ❑ Refund policy

____

____

By the Numbers:

- ❑ 188,000+ visitors per year
- ❑ 86,000+ acres
- ❑ Lat. 31.89434, Long. -104.82171
- ❑ 3 park entrances
- ❑ 3 visitor centers
- ❑ Highest elevation 8,751 ft.
- ❑ Lowest elevation 3,636 ft.

Attractions to Experience:

- ❑ Pine Springs VC Museum
- ❑ Pinery Nature Trail
- ❑ Hike Smith Spring Trail
- ❑ Hike Devils Hall Trail
- ❑ Stargaze at McDonald Observatory
- ❑ View wildlife at Manzanita Springs
- ❑ Look for birding opportunities
- ❑
- ❑
- ❑
- ❑
- ❑
- ❑
- ❑
- ❑
- ❑

Notes

____

____

____

____

____

____

____

____

____

____

____

Plan Your Trip:

- ❑ Staying at: _______________

  ____

  ____

- ❑ Phone __________________
- ❑ Reservations? ____Y ____N

  for dates ________________

- ❑ Check in time ___________
- ❑ Check out time __________
- ❑ Dog friendly _____Y ____N
- ❑ Max RV length ___________
- ❑ Dump Station location

  ____

  ____

- ❑ Distance from home

  miles: _________________

  hours: _________________

JOURNAL THE ADVENTURE

Why I went:

Dates I was in the park:

Where I stayed:

Who I went with:

How I got there: (circle all that apply)

Weather Experienced

Rate the Park

1 2 3 4 5

Will I go again?

Yes Maybe No

Memorable sights and experiences:

One thing I want to remember about this trip:

Something funny:

Something surprising:

Something disappointing:

TYPES OF PARKS

There are a variety of parks set aside as national treasure in the United States, so even if there isn't a National Park in your state, there are sure to be other ways you can experience history and nature. Begin by exploring the National Park website https://nps/gov or download their app.

- **National Parks** are set aside to protect large areas of land or water. There are limits on the commercial activities allowed.
- **National Preserves** also protect specific resources but allow activities like hunting, fishing, and the extraction of minerals and fuels.
- **National Reserves** are like national preserves but are not managed by the National Park Service, but instead managed by state and local authorities.
- **National Memorials** commemorate a historical subject or person. Some of the most famous are the World War II Memorial, Lincoln Memorial, and Mount Rushmore.
- **National Monuments** are smaller than national parks and preserve historic sites. There are currently 128 protected areas in the USA. Devils Tower National Monument, Statue of Liberty National Monument, and the Washington Monument are a few to choose from.
- **National Historic Sites** preserve places and commemorate people important to the nation's history.
- **National Historical Parks** are similar to Historic Sites but more substantial and more complex.
- **National Military Parks, National Battlefield Parks, National Battlefield Sites,** and **National Battlefields** are all associated with American military history.
- **National Recreational Areas** are protected areas set aside for recreational use. Some areas to visit include Lake Mead National Recreation Area at the Nevada Arizona border, or Boston Harbor Island National Recreational Area in Massachusetts.
- **National Lakeshores** and **National Seashores** preserve shorelines and islands while providing water-related recreation.
- **National Rivers and Wild and Scenic Riverways** protect land bordering streams that have been dammed, channelized, or altered in some way. As of November 2018, 209 rivers totaling 12,754 miles have wild and scenic status.
- **National Scenic Trails** are long-distance footpaths that wind through places of nature. The first is the Appalachian Trail, which was started in 1921 and completed in 1937.
- The **National Parkway** designation is given to a scenic roadway and a protected corridor of the surrounding parkland. The Natchez Trace Parkway, one of the most beautiful drives in America, was completed after 67 years and winds through Tennessee, Alabama, and Mississippi.
- **National Scenic Byways** are administered by the Federal Highway Administration and are identified according to six specific criteria: archaeological, scenic, natural, cultural, recreational, and historical.

MIDWEST REGION

- Indiana
- Michigan
- Minnesota
- Missouri
- Ohio

INDIANA DUNES NATIONAL PARK

State: Indiana — Date Est: February 15, 2019

Explore the Park Virtually: https://www.nps.gov/indu/index.htm

Address:
Visitor Center
1215 IN-49,
Porter, IN 46304

Open all year _____Y_____N

dates___________________

- ❑ Phone (219) 395-1882
- ❑ Park Hours ____________
- ❑ Entrance $ ____________
- ❑ Timed Entrance _________
- ❑ Camp Sites $ ___________
- ❑ RV Sites $ _____________
- ❑ Refund policy

____

____

By the Numbers:

- ❑ 2.1 million+ visitors per year
- ❑ 15,000+ acres
- ❑ Lat. 41.63378, Long. -87.05441
- ❑ 9+ park entrances
- ❑ 2 visitor centers
- ❑ Highest elevation 900 ft.
- ❑ Lowest elevation 597 ft.

Attractions to Experience:

- ❑ Take the Diana Dunes Dare ❑
- ❑ Self guided walking tour starts at Douglas VC ❑ ❑
- ❑ Hike Great Marsh Trail ❑
- ❑ Hike Outer Loop Trail, experience historical areas ❑ ❑
- ❑ Upland Trail to Pinhook Bog ❑
- ❑ 1933 World's Fair Century of Progress Homes ❑ ❑

Notes

____

____

____

____

____

____

____

____

____

____

____

Plan Your Trip:

- ❑ Staying at: ______________

  ____

  ____
- ❑ Phone _________________
- ❑ Reservations? ____Y ____N

  for dates _______________
- ❑ Check in time __________
- ❑ Check out time __________
- ❑ Dog friendly _____Y ____N
- ❑ Max RV length __________
- ❑ Dump Station location

  ____

  ____
- ❑ Distance from home

  miles: ________________

  hours: ________________

JOURNAL THE ADVENTURE

Why I went:

Dates I was in the park:

Where I stayed:

Who I went with:

How I got there: (circle all that apply)

Weather Experienced

Rate the Park

1 2 3 4 5

Will I go again?

Yes Maybe No

Memorable sights and experiences:

Something funny:

Something surprising:

Something disappointing:

One thing I want to remember about this trip:

ISLE ROYALE NATIONAL PARK

State: Michigan

Date Est: April 3, 1940

Explore the Park Virtually: https://www.nps.gov/isro/index.htm

Address:
Visitor Center
800 E Lakeshore Dr,
Houghton, MI 49931

Open all year _____Y_____N

dates___________________

- ❑ Phone (906) 482-0984
- ❑ Park Hours ____________
- ❑ Entrance $ ____________
- ❑ Timed Entrance _________
- ❑ Camp Sites $ __________
- ❑ RV Sites $ ____________
- ❑ Refund policy

____

____

By the Numbers:

- ❑ 26,000+ visitors per year
- ❑ 571,000+ acres
- ❑ Lat. 47.12295,
  Long. -88.56368
- ❑ 1 park entrance
- ❑ 2 visitor centers
- ❑ Highest elevation 1,394 ft.
- ❑ Lowest elevation 301 ft.

Attractions to Experience:

- ❑ Keweenaw Waterway Cruises ❑
- ❑ Take a tour on the MV Sandy ❑
- ❑ Ranger programs in Rock ❑
  Harbor Area ❑
- ❑ Windigo Whispers Ranger Tour ❑
- ❑ Take a hike in Rock Harbor or ❑
  Windigo ❑
- ❑ Explore the water on a boat or ❑
  kayak ❑

Notes

____

____

____

____

____

____

____

____

____

____

____

Plan Your Trip:

- ❑ Staying at: _____________

  ____

  ____

- ❑ Phone _______________
- ❑ Reservations? ____Y ____N

  for dates _____________

- ❑ Check in time __________
- ❑ Check out time __________
- ❑ Dog friendly _____Y ____N
- ❑ Max RV length __________
- ❑ Dump Station location

  ____

  ____

- ❑ Distance from home

  miles: _______________

  hours: _______________

JOURNAL THE ADVENTURE

Why I went:

Dates I was in the park:

Where I stayed:

Who I went with:

How I got there: (circle all that apply)

Weather Experienced

Rate the Park

1 2 3 4 5

Will I go again?

Yes Maybe No

Memorable sights and experiences:

Something funny:

Something surprising:

Something disappointing:

One thing I want to remember about this trip:

VOYAGEURS NATIONAL PARK

State: Minnesota

Date Est: April 8, 1975

Explore the Park Virtually: https://www.nps.gov/voya/index.htm

Address:
Rainy Lake Visitor Center
1797 Ut - 342,
International Falls, MN 56649

Open all year _____Y_____N

dates__________________

- ❑ Phone (906) 482-0984
- ❑ Park Hours ____________
- ❑ Entrance $ ____________
- ❑ Timed Entrance _________
- ❑ Camp Sites $ ___________
- ❑ RV Sites $ _____________
- ❑ Refund policy

____

____

By the Numbers:

- ❑ 232,000+ visitors per year
- ❑ 218,000+ acres
- ❑ Lat. 48.58471, Long. -93.16119
- ❑ 3 park entrances
- ❑ 3 visitor centers
- ❑ Highest elevation 1,410 ft.
- ❑ Lowest elevation 1,108 ft.

Attractions to Experience:

- ❑ Take a guided tour from Rainy Lake VC
- ❑ Take part in the Park's Hike to Health Trail Passport program
- ❑ Do a GPS Scavenger Hunt
- ❑ Visit Kettle Falls
- ❑ Experience Ellsworth Rock Gardens
- ❑ Take in winter activities

- ❑
- ❑
- ❑
- ❑
- ❑
- ❑
- ❑
- ❑
- ❑

Notes

____

____

____

____

____

____

____

____

____

____

____

Plan Your Trip:

- ❑ Staying at: ______________

  ____

  ____
- ❑ Phone ______________
- ❑ Reservations? ____Y ____N

  for dates ______________
- ❑ Check in time ___________
- ❑ Check out time __________
- ❑ Dog friendly _____Y ____N
- ❑ Max RV length ___________
- ❑ Dump Station location

  ____

  ____
- ❑ Distance from home

  miles: ______________

  hours: ______________

JOURNAL THE ADVENTURE

Why I went:

Dates I was in the park:

Where I stayed:

Who I went with:

How I got there: (circle all that apply)

Weather Experienced

Rate the Park

1 2 3 4 5

Will I go again?

Yes Maybe No

Memorable sights and experiences:

Something funny:

Something surprising:

Something disappointing:

One thing I want to remember about this trip:

GATEWAY ARCH NATIONAL PARK

State: Missouri — Date Est: February 22, 2018

Explore the Park Virtually: https://www.nps.gov/jeff/index.htm

Address:
11 N 4th St #1810,
St. Louis, MO 63102

Open all year _____Y_____N

dates___________________

- ❑ Phone (314) 655-1600
- ❑ Park Hours ____________
- ❑ Entrance $ ____________
- ❑ Timed Entrance _________
- ❑ Camp Sites $ __________
- ❑ RV Sites $ ____________
- ❑ Refund policy

____

____

By the Numbers:

- ❑ 2 million+ visitors per year
- ❑ 192+ acres
- ❑ Lat. 38.62696, Long. -90.1855
- ❑ 1 park entrance
- ❑ 1 visitor center
- ❑ Highest elevation 630 ft.
- ❑ Lowest elevation 446 ft.

Attractions to Experience:

- ❑ Tram ride to the top
- ❑ Visit the Museum under the Arch
- ❑ View the film – Monument to Dream
- ❑ Junior ranger program
- ❑ Take a riverboat cruise
- ❑ Ranger tour of the Old Courthouse

- ❑
- ❑
- ❑
- ❑
- ❑
- ❑
- ❑
- ❑
- ❑

Notes

____

____

____

____

____

____

____

____

____

____

____

Plan Your Trip:

- ❑ Staying at: ______________

  ____

  ____
- ❑ Phone ________________
- ❑ Reservations? ____Y ____N

  for dates ________________
- ❑ Check in time __________
- ❑ Check out time __________
- ❑ Dog friendly _____Y ____N
- ❑ Max RV length ___________
- ❑ Dump Station location

  ____

  ____
- ❑ Distance from home

  miles: ________________

  hours: ________________

JOURNAL THE ADVENTURE

Why I went:

Dates I was in the park:

Where I stayed:

Who I went with:

How I got there: (circle all that apply)

Weather Experienced

Rate the Park

1 2 3 4 5

Will I go again?

Yes Maybe No

Memorable sights and experiences:

One thing I want to remember about this trip:

Something funny:

Something surprising:

Something disappointing:

CUYAHOGA VALLEY NATIONAL PARK

State: Ohio

Date Est: October 11, 2000

Explore the Park Virtually: https://www.nps.gov/cuva/index.htm

Address:
Boston Mill VC
5793 Boston Mills Rd,
Peninsula, OH 44264

Open all year _____Y_____N

dates_________________

- ❑ Phone (330) 657-2752
- ❑ Park Hours ___________
- ❑ Entrance $ ___________
- ❑ Timed Entrance _________
- ❑ Camp Sites $ __________
- ❑ RV Sites $ ___________
- ❑ Refund policy

____

____

By the Numbers:

- ❑ 2.2 million+ visitors per year
- ❑ 32+ acres
- ❑ Lat. 41.2626, Long. -81.56031
- ❑ MANY park entrances
- ❑ 3 visitor centers
- ❑ Highest elevation 1,164 ft.
- ❑ Lowest elevation 590 ft.

Attractions to Experience:

- ❑ Walk Towpath Trail
- ❑ Take a ride on Cuyahoga Valley scenic railroad from one of 8 stops
- ❑ Access the river from Lock 29 or Lock 39
- ❑ View Brandywine Falls
- ❑ See Everett Covered Bridge
- ❑ Visit Hunt House in Everett

- ❑
- ❑
- ❑
- ❑
- ❑
- ❑
- ❑
- ❑
- ❑

Notes

____

____

____

____

____

____

____

____

____

____

____

Plan Your Trip:

- ❑ Staying at: ______________

  ____

  ____

- ❑ Phone ______________
- ❑ Reservations? ____Y ____N

  for dates ______________

- ❑ Check in time __________
- ❑ Check out time __________
- ❑ Dog friendly _____Y ____N
- ❑ Max RV length __________
- ❑ Dump Station location

  ____

  ____

- ❑ Distance from home

  miles: ______________

  hours: ______________

JOURNAL THE ADVENTURE

Why I went:

Dates I was in the park:

Where I stayed:

Who I went with:

How I got there: (circle all that apply)

Weather Experienced

Rate the Park

1 2 3 4 5

Will I go again?

Yes Maybe No

Memorable sights and experiences:

Something funny:

Something surprising:

Something disappointing:

One thing I want to remember about this trip:

NATIONAL PARK Properties with LODGES

- ❑ Badlands National Park
- ❑ Big Bend National Park
- ❑ Blue Ridge Parkway
- ❑ Bryce Canyon National Park
- ❑ Buffalo National River
- ❑ Canyon de Chelly National Monument
- ❑ Crater Lake National Park
- ❑ Cuyahoga Valley National Park
- ❑ Death Valley National Park
- ❑ Glacier National Park
- ❑ Glacier Bay National Park & Preserve
- ❑ Glen Canon National Recreation Area
- ❑ Golden Gate National Recreation Area
- ❑ Grand Canyon National Park
- ❑ Grand Teton National Park
- ❑ Hawaii Volcanoes National Park
- ❑ Isle Royale National Park
- ❑ Lake Mead National Recreation Area
- ❑ Lassen Volcanic National Park
- ❑ Mammoth Cave National Park
- ❑ Mesa Verde National Park
- ❑ Mount Rainier National Park
- ❑ North Cascades National Park
- ❑ Olympic National Park
- ❑ Oregon Caves National Monument
- ❑ Ozark National Scenic Riverways
- ❑ Shenandoah National River
- ❑ Sequoia & Kings Canyon National Park
- ❑ Virgin Islands National Park
- ❑ Voyageurs National Park
- ❑ Yellowstone National Park
- ❑ Yosemite National Park
- ❑ Zion National Park

ROCKY MOUNTAIN REGION

- Colorado
- Montana
- North Dakota
- South Dakota
- Utah
- Wyoming

BLACK CANYON OF THE GUNNISON N. P.

State: Colorado   Date Est: October 21, 1999

Explore the Park Virtually: https://www.nps.gov/blca/index.htm

Address:
South Rim VC
10346 CO-347,
Montrose, CO 81401

Open all year _____Y_____N

dates____________________

- ❑ Phone (970) 641-2337 x205
- ❑ Park Hours ____________
- ❑ Entrance $ ____________
- ❑ Timed Entrance _________
- ❑ Camp Sites $ ___________
- ❑ RV Sites $ _____________
- ❑ Refund policy

____

____

By the Numbers:

- ❑ 430,000+ visitors per year
- ❑ 30,000+ acres
- ❑ Lat. 38.55499, Long -107.68658
- ❑ 2 park entrances
- ❑ 1 visitor center
- ❑ Highest elevation 8,289 ft.
- ❑ Lowest elevation 5,440 ft.

Attractions to Experience:

- ❑ Start at the South Rim VC ❑
- ❑ Take the South Rim Drive ❑
- ❑ Snap a pic at Tomichi Overlook ❑
- ❑ North Rim Ranger Station and the North Vista Trail are closed in winter ❑ ❑ ❑
- ❑ Take a ranger led geology walk ❑
- ❑ Walk the Cedar Point Nature Trail ❑ ❑

Notes

____

____

____

____

____

____

____

____

____

____

____

Plan Your Trip:

- ❑ Staying at: ______________

  ____

  ____
- ❑ Phone _________________
- ❑ Reservations? ____Y ____N

  for dates ________________
- ❑ Check in time __________
- ❑ Check out time __________
- ❑ Dog friendly _____Y ____N
- ❑ Max RV length __________
- ❑ Dump Station location

  ____

  ____
- ❑ Distance from home

  miles: _________________

  hours: _________________

JOURNAL THE ADVENTURE

Why I went:

Dates I was in the park:

Where I stayed:

Who I went with:

How I got there: (circle all that apply)

Weather Experienced

Rate the Park

1 2 3 4 5

Will I go again?

Yes Maybe No

Memorable sights and experiences:

Something funny:

Something surprising:

Something disappointing:

One thing I want to remember about this trip:

GREAT SAND DUNES NATIONAL PARK & PRESERVE

State: Colorado

Date Est: September 24, 2004

Explore the Park Virtually: https://www.nps.gov/grsa/index.htm

Address:
11999 CO-150,
Mosca, CO 81146

Open all year _____Y_____N

dates__________________

- ❑ Phone (719) 378-6395
- ❑ Park Hours ____________
- ❑ Entrance $ ____________
- ❑ Timed Entrance _________
- ❑ Camp Sites $ ___________
- ❑ RV Sites $ _____________
- ❑ Refund policy

____

____

By the Numbers:

- ❑ 527,000+ visitors per year
- ❑ 107,000+ acres
- ❑ Lat. 37.73299, Long -105.5125
- ❑ 1 park entrance
- ❑ 1 visitor center
- ❑ Highest elevation 13,604 ft.
- ❑ Lowest elevation 7,520 ft.

Attractions to Experience:

- ❑ Visit the Dunefield
- ❑ Catch a surge flow at Medano Creek
- ❑ Go off-roading with your 4WD
- ❑ Stargaze at this certified Dark Sky Park
- ❑ Go sand sledding or surfing
- ❑ Hike Montville Nature Trail or Mosca Pass Trail

- ❑
- ❑
- ❑
- ❑
- ❑
- ❑
- ❑
- ❑
- ❑

Notes

____

____

____

____

____

____

____

____

____

____

____

Plan Your Trip:

- ❑ Staying at: ______________

  ____

  ____

- ❑ Phone _______________
- ❑ Reservations? ____Y ____N

  for dates _______________

- ❑ Check in time __________
- ❑ Check out time __________
- ❑ Dog friendly _____Y ____N
- ❑ Max RV length ___________
- ❑ Dump Station location

  ____

  ____

- ❑ Distance from home

  miles: _________________

  hours: ________________

JOURNAL THE ADVENTURE

Why I went:

Dates I was in the park:

Where I stayed:

Who I went with:

How I got there: (circle all that apply)

Weather Experienced

Rate the Park

1 2 3 4 5

Will I go again?

Yes Maybe No

Memorable sights and experiences:

Something funny:

Something surprising:

Something disappointing:

One thing I want to remember about this trip:

MESA VERDE NATIONAL PARK

State: Colorado

Date Est: June 29, 1906

Explore the Park Virtually: https://www.nps.gov/meve/index.htm

Address:
35853 Rd H.5,
Mancos, CO 81328

Open all year _____Y_____N

dates___________________

- ❑ Phone (970) 529-4465
- ❑ Park Hours ____________
- ❑ Entrance $ ____________
- ❑ Timed Entrance _________
- ❑ Camp Sites $ __________
- ❑ RV Sites $ ____________
- ❑ Refund policy

____

____

By the Numbers:

- ❑ 550,000+ visitors per year
- ❑ 52,000+ acres
- ❑ Lat. 37.33575,
  Long -108.40791
- ❑ 4 park entrances
- ❑ 2 visitor centers
- ❑ Highest elevation 8,571 ft.
- ❑ Lowest elevation 6,015 ft.

Attractions to Experience:

- ❑ Visit Spruce Tree Overlook
- ❑ Drive Mesa Top Loop Road, audio tour and take the short trails to:
- ❑ Square Tower House Overlook
- ❑ Sun Point View
- ❑ Sun Temple
- ❑ See Fair View Community sites
- ❑ Cliff Palace Overlook

- ❑
- ❑
- ❑
- ❑
- ❑
- ❑
- ❑
- ❑
- ❑

Notes

____

____

____

____

____

____

____

____

____

____

____

Plan Your Trip:

- ❑ Staying at: ______________

  ____

  ____
- ❑ Phone ________________
- ❑ Reservations? ____Y ____N

  for dates ______________
- ❑ Check in time __________
- ❑ Check out time __________
- ❑ Dog friendly _____Y ____N
- ❑ Max RV length __________
- ❑ Dump Station location

  ____

  ____
- ❑ Distance from home

  miles: ________________

  hours: ________________

JOURNAL THE ADVENTURE

Why I went:

Dates I was in the park:

Where I stayed:

Who I went with:

How I got there: (circle all that apply)

Weather Experienced

Rate the Park

1 2 3 4 5

Will I go again?

Yes Maybe No

Memorable sights and experiences:

Something funny:

Something surprising:

Something disappointing:

One thing I want to remember about this trip:

ROCKY MOUNTAIN NATIONAL PARK

State: Colorado

Date Est: January 26, 1915

Explore the Park Virtually: https://www.nps.gov/romo/index.htm

Address:
Beaver Meadow VC
1000 US-36,
Estes Park, CO 80517

Open all year _____Y_____N

dates___________________

- ❑ Phone (970) 586-1206
- ❑ Park Hours ____________
- ❑ Entrance $ ____________
- ❑ Timed Entrance _________
- ❑ Camp Sites $ __________
- ❑ RV Sites $ ____________
- ❑ Refund policy

____

____

By the Numbers:

- ❑ 4.6 million+ visitors per year
- ❑ 265,000+ acres
- ❑ Lat. 40.36618,
  Long -105.56081
- ❑ 7 park entrances
- ❑ 7 visitor centers
- ❑ Highest elevation 14,259 ft.
- ❑ Lowest elevation 7,630 ft.

Attractions to Experience:

- ❑ Drive Old Fall River Road
- ❑ Snap a pic of Chasm Falls
- ❑ Picnic in Hidden Valley
- ❑ Hike Bierstadt Lake
- ❑ Hike Alberta Falls
- ❑ Take Lily Lake Loop
- ❑ Take Sprague Lake Loop
- ❑ Explore Holzwarth Historic site
- ❑ Explore Alpine Tundra Trail
- ❑
- ❑
- ❑
- ❑
- ❑
- ❑
- ❑
- ❑
- ❑

Notes

____

____

____

____

____

____

____

____

____

____

____

Plan Your Trip:

- ❑ Staying at: ______________
  ____
  ____
- ❑ Phone ________________
- ❑ Reservations? ____Y ____N
  for dates ______________
- ❑ Check in time __________
- ❑ Check out time _________
- ❑ Dog friendly _____Y ____N
- ❑ Max RV length __________
- ❑ Dump Station location
  ____
  ____
- ❑ Distance from home
  miles: ________________
  hours: ________________

JOURNAL THE ADVENTURE

Why I went:

Dates I was in the park:

Where I stayed:

Who I went with:

How I got there: (circle all that apply)

Weather Experienced

Rate the Park

1 2 3 4 5

Will I go again?

Yes Maybe No

Memorable sights and experiences:

Something funny:

Something surprising:

Something disappointing:

One thing I want to remember about this trip:

GLACIER NATIONAL PARK

State: Montana

Date Est: May 11, 1910

Explore the Park Virtually: https://www.nps.gov/glac/index.htm

Address:
Apgar Visitor Center
Going-to-the-Sun Rd,
West Glacier, MT 59936

Open all year _____Y_____N

dates___________________

- ❑ Phone (406) 888-7800
- ❑ Park Hours ____________
- ❑ Entrance $ ____________
- ❑ Timed Entrance _________
- ❑ Camp Sites $ ___________
- ❑ RV Sites $ _____________
- ❑ Refund policy

____

____

By the Numbers:

- ❑ 3 million+ visitors per year
- ❑ 1 million+ acres
- ❑ Lat. 48.52307, Long -113.98851
- ❑ 7 park entrances
- ❑ 3 visitor centers
- ❑ Highest elevation 10,466 ft.
- ❑ Lowest elevation 3,150 ft.

Attractions to Experience:

- ❑ Apgar Village, Sunset on Lake McDonald
- ❑ Lake McDonald Lodge (1913)
- ❑ Many Glacier Hotel (1914)
- ❑ St. Mary VC
- ❑ Logan Pass VC
- ❑ Drive Going-to-the-Sun Road
- ❑ Apgar Campground Amphitheater evening program

❑
❑
❑
❑
❑
❑
❑
❑
❑

Notes

____

____

____

____

____

____

____

____

____

____

____

Plan Your Trip:

- ❑ Staying at: _______________

  ____

  ____

- ❑ Phone _________________
- ❑ Reservations? ____Y ____N

  for dates _________________

- ❑ Check in time ___________
- ❑ Check out time __________
- ❑ Dog friendly _____Y ____N
- ❑ Max RV length ___________
- ❑ Dump Station location

  ____

  ____

- ❑ Distance from home

  miles: _________________

  hours: _________________

JOURNAL THE ADVENTURE

Why I went:

Dates I was in the park:

Where I stayed:

Who I went with:

How I got there: (circle all that apply)

Weather Experienced

Rate the Park

1 2 3 4 5

Will I go again?

Yes Maybe No

Memorable sights and experiences:

Something funny:

Something surprising:

Something disappointing:

One thing I want to remember about this trip:

THEODORE ROOSEVELT NATIONAL PARK

State: North Dakota   Date Est: November 10, 1978

Explore the Park Virtually: https://www.nps.gov/thro/index.htm

Address:
South Unit VC
315 2nd Ave,
Medora, ND 58645

Open all year _____Y_____N

dates____________________

- ❑ Phone (701) 623-4466
- ❑ Park Hours ____________
- ❑ Entrance $ ____________
- ❑ Timed Entrance _________
- ❑ Camp Sites $ ___________
- ❑ RV Sites $ _____________
- ❑ Refund policy

____

____

By the Numbers:

- ❑ 691,000+ visitors per year
- ❑ 70,000+ acres
- ❑ Lat. 46.91649, Long -103.52621
- ❑ 3 park entrances
- ❑ 3 visitor centers
- ❑ Highest elevation 2,865 ft.
- ❑ Lowest elevation 2,240 ft.

Attractions to Experience:

- ❑ North Unit VC
- ❑ South Unit VC
- ❑ Maltese Cross Cabin
- ❑ Peaceful Valley dude ranch
- ❑ Old East Entrance station
- ❑ River Bend Overlook
- ❑ Skyline Vista trail / overlook
- ❑ Snap a pic Badlands overlook
- ❑ Find a Cannonball Concretion
- ❑
- ❑
- ❑
- ❑
- ❑
- ❑
- ❑
- ❑
- ❑

Notes

____

____

____

____

____

____

____

____

____

____

____

Plan Your Trip:

- ❑ Staying at: _______________

  ____

  ____
- ❑ Phone _________________
- ❑ Reservations? ____Y ____N

  for dates _________________
- ❑ Check in time ___________
- ❑ Check out time __________
- ❑ Dog friendly _____Y ____N
- ❑ Max RV length ___________
- ❑ Dump Station location

  ____

  ____
- ❑ Distance from home

  miles: __________________

  hours: _________________

JOURNAL THE ADVENTURE

Why I went:

Dates I was in the park:

Where I stayed:

Who I went with:

How I got there: (circle all that apply)

Weather Experienced

Rate the Park

1 2 3 4 5

Will I go again?

Yes Maybe No

Memorable sights and experiences:

Something funny:

Something surprising:

Something disappointing:

One thing I want to remember about this trip:

BADLANDS NATIONAL PARK

State: South Dakota Date Est: November 10, 1978

Explore the Park Virtually: https://www.nps.gov/badl/index.htm

Address:
Ben Reifel VC
25216 SD-240,
Interior, SD 57750

Open all year _____Y_____N

dates____________________

- ❑ Phone (605) 433-5361
- ❑ Park Hours ____________
- ❑ Entrance $ ____________
- ❑ Timed Entrance ________
- ❑ Camp Sites $ ___________
- ❑ RV Sites $ ____________
- ❑ Refund policy
  ____
  ____

By the Numbers:

- ❑ 970,000+ visitors per year
- ❑ 242,000+ acres
- ❑ Lat. 43.74908, Long -101.94164
- ❑ 3 park entrances
- ❑ 2 visitor centers
- ❑ Highest elevation 3,832 ft.
- ❑ Lowest elevation 2,460 ft.

Attractions to Experience:

- ❑ Ancient Hunters Overlook
- ❑ Panorama Point Overlook
- ❑ Pinnacles Overlook
- ❑ Quinn Road Prairie Dog Town
- ❑ Fossil Exhibit Trail
- ❑ Stargazing - Badlands Astronomy Festival
- ❑ Door Trail Geology walk
- ❑ Fossil Preparation Lab

- ❑
- ❑
- ❑
- ❑
- ❑
- ❑
- ❑
- ❑
- ❑

Notes

____
____
____
____
____
____
____
____
____
____
____

Plan Your Trip:

- ❑ Staying at: ______________
  ____
  ____
- ❑ Phone ________________
- ❑ Reservations? ____Y ____N
  for dates ______________
- ❑ Check in time __________
- ❑ Check out time __________
- ❑ Dog friendly _____Y ____N
- ❑ Max RV length __________
- ❑ Dump Station location
  ____
  ____
- ❑ Distance from home
  miles: ________________
  hours: ________________

JOURNAL THE ADVENTURE

Why I went:

Dates I was in the park:

Where I stayed:

Who I went with:

How I got there: (circle all that apply)

Weather Experienced

Rate the Park

1 2 3 4 5

Will I go again?

Yes Maybe No

Memorable sights and experiences:

Something funny:

Something surprising:

Something disappointing:

One thing I want to remember about this trip:

WIND CAVE NATIONAL PARK

State: South Dakota   Date Est: January 9, 1903

Explore the Park Virtually: https://www.nps.gov/wica/index.htm

Address:
26611 US-385,
Hot Springs, SD, 57747

Open all year _____Y_____N

dates___________________

- ❑ Phone (605) 745-4600
- ❑ Park Hours ____________
- ❑ Entrance $ ____________
- ❑ Timed Entrance _________
- ❑ Camp Sites $ ___________
- ❑ RV Sites $ _____________
- ❑ Refund policy

____

____

By the Numbers:

- ❑ 615,000+ visitors per year
- ❑ 28,000+ acres
- ❑ Lat. 43. 55655, Long -103.4783
- ❑ 1 park entrance
- ❑ 1 visitor center
- ❑ Highest elevation 5,013 ft.
- ❑ Lowest elevation 3,559 ft.

Attractions to Experience:

- ❑ Hike Elk Mountain Nature Trail ❑
- ❑ Take the Geology Driving Tour ❑
- ❑ Explore Rankin Ridge Nature Tr ❑
- ❑ Visit Wind River Cave's natural ❑ entrance ❑
- ❑ Garden of Eden Cave Tour ❑
- ❑ Natural Entrance Cave Tour ❑
- ❑ Fairgrounds cave tour (stairs) ❑
- ❑ ❑

Notes

____

____

____

____

____

____

____

____

____

____

____

Plan Your Trip:

- ❑ Staying at: _______________

  ____

  ____
- ❑ Phone _______________
- ❑ Reservations? ____Y ____N

  for dates _______________
- ❑ Check in time ___________
- ❑ Check out time __________
- ❑ Dog friendly _____Y ____N
- ❑ Max RV length ___________
- ❑ Dump Station location

  ____

  ____
- ❑ Distance from home

  miles: _______________

  hours: _______________

JOURNAL THE ADVENTURE

Why I went:

Dates I was in the park:

Where I stayed:

Who I went with:

How I got there: (circle all that apply)

Weather Experienced

Rate the Park

1 2 3 4 5

Will I go again?

Yes Maybe No

Memorable sights and experiences:

Something funny:

Something surprising:

Something disappointing:

One thing I want to remember about this trip:

ARCHES NATIONAL PARK

State: Utah — Date Est: November 12, 1971

Explore the Park Virtually: https://www.nps.gov/arch/index.htm

Address:
Arches Entrance Rd / Arches Scenic Dr,
Moab, UT 84532

Open all year _____Y_____N

dates__________________

- ❑ Phone (435) 719-2299
- ❑ Park Hours ____________
- ❑ Entrance $ ____________
- ❑ Timed Entrance _________
- ❑ Camp Sites $ __________
- ❑ RV Sites $ ____________
- ❑ Refund policy

____

____

By the Numbers:

- ❑ 1.6 million+ visitors per year
- ❑ 76,000+ acres
- ❑ Lat. 38.61658, Long -109.61984
- ❑ 1 park entrance
- ❑ 1 visitor center
- ❑ Highest elevation 5,653 ft.
- ❑ Lowest elevation 4,085 ft.

Attractions to Experience:

- ❑ Park Ave Viewpoint
- ❑ Ranger led Stargazing
- ❑ Snap a pic of Balanced Rock
- ❑ Panorama Point
- ❑ Trail to Double Arch
- ❑ Sunrise at Moab Fault
- ❑ Hike Delicate Arch Trail
- ❑ Skyline Arch at Sunset
- ❑ Theater at Arches VC
- ❑
- ❑
- ❑
- ❑
- ❑
- ❑
- ❑
- ❑
- ❑

Notes

____

____

____

____

____

____

____

____

____

____

____

Plan Your Trip:

- ❑ Staying at: ______________

  ____

  ____
- ❑ Phone ________________
- ❑ Reservations? ____Y ____N

  for dates ________________
- ❑ Check in time ___________
- ❑ Check out time __________
- ❑ Dog friendly _____Y ____N
- ❑ Max RV length ___________
- ❑ Dump Station location

  ____

  ____
- ❑ Distance from home

  miles: _________________

  hours: _________________

JOURNAL THE ADVENTURE

Why I went:

Dates I was in the park:

Where I stayed:

Who I went with:

How I got there: (circle all that apply)

Weather Experienced

Rate the Park

1 2 3 4 5

Will I go again?

Yes Maybe No

Memorable sights and experiences:

One thing I want to remember about this trip:

Something funny:

Something surprising:

Something disappointing:

BRYCE CANYON NATIONAL PARK

State: Utah — Date Est: February 25, 1928

Explore the Park Virtually: https://www.nps.gov/brca/index.htm

Address:
UT-63,
Bryce Canyon City, UT 84764

Open all year _____Y_____N

dates___________________

- ❑ Phone (435) 834-5322
- ❑ Park Hours ____________
- ❑ Entrance $ ____________
- ❑ Timed Entrance _________
- ❑ Camp Sites $ ___________
- ❑ RV Sites $ _____________
- ❑ Refund policy

____

____

By the Numbers:

- ❑ 2.5 million+ visitors per year
- ❑ 35,000+ acres
- ❑ Lat. 37.64036, Long -112.16958
- ❑ 1 park entrance
- ❑ 1 visitor center
- ❑ Highest elevation 9,105 ft.
- ❑ Lowest elevation 6,620 ft.

Attractions to Experience:

- ❑ Bryce Point Viewpoint ❑
- ❑ Inspiration Point ❑
- ❑ Snap a pic at Sunset Point ❑
- ❑ Take the Southern Scenic Drive ❑
- ❑ Visit Natural Bridge ❑
- ❑ Mossy Cave Trail ❑
- ❑ Park film "A Song of Seasons" ❑
- ❑ Stargazing / Int'l Dark Sky Park ❑
- ❑ Ride the shared-use path ❑

Notes

____

____

____

____

____

____

____

____

____

____

____

Plan Your Trip:

- ❑ Staying at: ______________

  ____

  ____
- ❑ Phone _________________
- ❑ Reservations? ____Y ____N

  for dates ________________
- ❑ Check in time __________
- ❑ Check out time __________
- ❑ Dog friendly _____Y ____N
- ❑ Max RV length ___________
- ❑ Dump Station location

  ____

  ____
- ❑ Distance from home

  miles: __________________

  hours: __________________

JOURNAL THE ADVENTURE

Why I went:

Dates I was in the park:

Where I stayed:

Who I went with:

How I got there: (circle all that apply)

Weather Experienced

Rate the Park

1 2 3 4 5

Will I go again?

Yes Maybe No

Memorable sights and experiences:

Something funny:

Something surprising:

Something disappointing:

One thing I want to remember about this trip:

CANYONLANDS NATIONAL PARK

State: Utah

Date Est: September 12, 1964

Explore the Park Virtually: https://www.nps.gov/cany/index.htm

Address:
Island in the Sky VC
Grand View Point Rd,
Moab, UT 84532

Open all year _____Y_____N

dates___________________

- ❑ Phone (435) 259-4712
- ❑ Park Hours ____________
- ❑ Entrance $ ____________
- ❑ Timed Entrance _________
- ❑ Camp Sites $ ___________
- ❑ RV Sites $ ____________
- ❑ Refund policy

____

____

By the Numbers:

- ❑ 733,000+ visitors per year
- ❑ 337,000+ acres
- ❑ Lat. 38.45983, Long -109.82098
- ❑ 2 park entrances
- ❑ 3 visitor centers
- ❑ Highest elevation 7,120 ft.
- ❑ Lowest elevation 3,730 ft.

Attractions to Experience:

- ❑ Island in the Sky mesa stops
- ❑ Sunrise at Mesa Arch
- ❑ Candlestick Tower Overlook
- ❑ Canyonlands' Cave Springs Tr.
- ❑ Horseshoe Canyon rock markings
- ❑ Green River Overlook
- ❑ Experience Shafer Trail road (4WD required)

- ❑
- ❑
- ❑
- ❑
- ❑
- ❑
- ❑
- ❑
- ❑

Notes

____

____

____

____

____

____

____

____

____

____

____

Plan Your Trip:

- ❑ Staying at: _______________

  ____

  ____

- ❑ Phone _________________
- ❑ Reservations? ____Y ____N

  for dates ________________

- ❑ Check in time __________
- ❑ Check out time __________
- ❑ Dog friendly _____Y ____N
- ❑ Max RV length __________
- ❑ Dump Station location

  ____

  ____

- ❑ Distance from home

  miles: _________________

  hours: _________________

JOURNAL THE ADVENTURE

Why I went:

Dates I was in the park:

Where I stayed:

Who I went with:

How I got there: (circle all that apply)

Weather Experienced

Rate the Park

1 2 3 4 5

Will I go again?

Yes Maybe No

Memorable sights and experiences:

Something funny:

Something surprising:

Something disappointing:

One thing I want to remember about this trip:

CAPITOL REEF NATIONAL PARK

State: Utah

Date Est: December 18, 1971

Explore the Park Virtually: https://www.nps.gov/care/index.htm

Address:
Camp Ground Rd,
Torrey, UT, 84775

Open all year _____Y_____N

dates__________________

- ❑ Phone (435) 425-3791
- ❑ Park Hours ____________
- ❑ Entrance $ ____________
- ❑ Timed Entrance _________
- ❑ Camp Sites $ ___________
- ❑ RV Sites $ ____________
- ❑ Refund policy

____

____

By the Numbers:

- ❑ 1.2 million+ visitors per year
- ❑ 241,000+ acres
- ❑ Lat. 38.29146, Long -111.26204
- ❑ 4 park entrances
- ❑ 1 visitor center
- ❑ Highest elevation 7,041 ft.
- ❑ Lowest elevation 3,877 ft.

Attractions to Experience:

- ❑ Take the 7.9 mile scenic drive
- ❑ Snap a pic at Panorama Point
- ❑ See the Fremont Culture petroglyphs
- ❑ Visit Frutia Valley and the Gifford Farm
- ❑ Stargaze / Int'l Dark Sky Park
- ❑ Hike Goosenecks Trail
- ❑ Sunset Point Trail at dusk
- ❑
- ❑
- ❑
- ❑
- ❑
- ❑
- ❑
- ❑
- ❑

Notes

____

____

____

____

____

____

____

____

____

____

____

Plan Your Trip:

- ❑ Staying at: ______________

  ____

  ____
- ❑ Phone ________________
- ❑ Reservations? ____Y ____N

  for dates ________________
- ❑ Check in time __________
- ❑ Check out time __________
- ❑ Dog friendly _____Y ____N
- ❑ Max RV length ___________
- ❑ Dump Station location

  ____

  ____
- ❑ Distance from home

  miles: _________________

  hours: _________________

JOURNAL THE ADVENTURE

Why I went:

Dates I was in the park:

Where I stayed:

Who I went with:

How I got there: (circle all that apply)

Weather Experienced

Rate the Park

1 2 3 4 5

Will I go again?

Yes Maybe No

Memorable sights and experiences:

Something funny:

Something surprising:

Something disappointing:

One thing I want to remember about this trip:

ZION NATIONAL PARK

State: Utah

Date Est: November 19, 1919

Explore the Park Virtually: https://www.nps.gov/zion/index.htm

Address:
1 Zion Park Blvd,
Springdale, UT 84767

Open all year _____Y_____N

dates___________________

- ❑ Phone (435) 425-3791
- ❑ Park Hours ____________
- ❑ Entrance $ ____________
- ❑ Timed Entrance _________
- ❑ Camp Sites $ ___________
- ❑ RV Sites $ _____________
- ❑ Refund policy

____

____

By the Numbers:

- ❑ 4.4 million+ visitors per year
- ❑ 147,000+ acres
- ❑ Lat. 37.19995, Long -112.9876
- ❑ 6 park entrances
- ❑ 3 visitor centers
- ❑ Highest elevation 7,810 ft.
- ❑ Lowest elevation 3,666 ft.

Attractions to Experience:

- ❑ Visit the Human History Museum
- ❑ Bike the Pa'rus Trail
- ❑ Take a Ranger-led walk on the Grotto Trail
- ❑ Sunset at Kolob Canyons Vpt
- ❑ Stargazing / Int'l Dark Sky Park
- ❑ Hike Archeology Trail
- ❑ Drive Mt Carmel Highway

❑
❑
❑
❑
❑
❑
❑
❑
❑

Notes

____

____

____

____

____

____

____

____

____

____

____

Plan Your Trip:

- ❑ Staying at: _______________

  ____

  ____

- ❑ Phone _________________
- ❑ Reservations? ____Y ____N

  for dates _______________

- ❑ Check in time __________
- ❑ Check out time __________
- ❑ Dog friendly _____Y ____N
- ❑ Max RV length __________
- ❑ Dump Station location

  ____

  ____

- ❑ Distance from home

  miles: _______________

  hours: _______________

JOURNAL THE ADVENTURE

Why I went:

Dates I was in the park:

Where I stayed:

Who I went with:

How I got there: (circle all that apply)

Weather Experienced

Rate the Park

1 2 3 4 5

Will I go again?

Yes Maybe No

Memorable sights and experiences:

Something funny:

Something surprising:

Something disappointing:

One thing I want to remember about this trip:

GRAND TETON NATIONAL PARK

State: Wyoming　　Date Est: February 26, 1929

Explore the Park Virtually: https://www.nps.gov/grte/index.htm

Address:
Craig Thomas Discovery & VC
1 Teton Park Rd,
Moose, WY 83012

Open all year _____Y_____N

dates___________________

- ❑ Phone (307) 739-3399
- ❑ Park Hours ____________
- ❑ Entrance $ ____________
- ❑ Timed Entrance _________
- ❑ Camp Sites $ ___________
- ❑ RV Sites $ _____________
- ❑ Refund policy

____

____

By the Numbers:

- ❑ 3.4 million+ visitors per year
- ❑ 310,000+ acres
- ❑ Lat. 43.65341,
  Long -110.71855
- ❑ 3 park entrances
- ❑ 5 visitor centers
- ❑ Highest elevation 13,775 ft.
- ❑ Lowest elevation 6,320 ft.

Attractions to Experience:

- ❑ Visit Jackson Lake Overlook ❑
- ❑ Channel Ansel Adams at Snake ❑
  River Overlook (self-guided tour) ❑
- ❑ Visit Jackson Lake Lodge ❑
- ❑ Menors Ferry Historic District ❑
- ❑ Catch wildlife at Oxbow Bend ❑
- ❑ Hike Christian Pond Loop ❑
- ❑ Drive Signal Mt. Summit Road ❑
- ❑ Heron Pond-Swan Lake Loop ❑

Plan Your Trip:

- ❑ Staying at: _______________

  ____

  ____
- ❑ Phone _________________
- ❑ Reservations? ____Y ____N

  for dates ________________
- ❑ Check in time ___________
- ❑ Check out time __________
- ❑ Dog friendly _____Y ____N
- ❑ Max RV length ___________
- ❑ Dump Station location

  ____

  ____
- ❑ Distance from home

  miles: _________________

  hours: _________________

Notes

____

____

____

____

____

____

____

____

____

____

____

JOURNAL THE ADVENTURE

Why I went:

Dates I was in the park:

Where I stayed:

Who I went with:

How I got there: (circle all that apply)

Weather Experienced

Rate the Park

1 2 3 4 5

Will I go again?

Yes Maybe No

Memorable sights and experiences:

Something funny:

Something surprising:

Something disappointing:

One thing I want to remember about this trip:

YELLOWSTONE NATIONAL PARK

State: Wyoming / Montana　　Date Est: March 1, 1872

Explore the Park Virtually: https://www.nps.gov/yell/index.htm

Address:
Grant Visitor Center
Grant Village Rd,
Yellowstone National Park, WY
82190

Open all year _____Y_____N

dates___________________

- ❑ Phone (307) 242-2650
- ❑ Park Hours ____________
- ❑ Entrance $ ____________
- ❑ Timed Entrance _________
- ❑ Camp Sites $ ___________
- ❑ RV Sites $ ____________
- ❑ Refund policy

____

____

By the Numbers:

- ❑ 4 million+ visitors per year
- ❑ 2.2 million+ acres
- ❑ Lat. 44.3936,
  Long -110.55633
- ❑ 5 park entrances
- ❑ 10 visitor centers
- ❑ Highest elevation 11,358 ft.
- ❑ Lowest elevation 5,282 ft.

Attractions to Experience:

- ❑ Watch Old Faithful Geyser ❑
- ❑ Abyss Pool ❑
- ❑ Castle Geyser ❑
- ❑ Eat at Old Faithful Inn ❑
- ❑ Hike Grand Prismatic Overlook ❑
  Trail ❑
- ❑ Take Mud Volcano Trail ❑
- ❑ Explore Ft Yellowstone Historic ❑
  District at Mammoth Hot Springs ❑

Notes

____

____

____

____

____

____

____

____

____

____

____

Plan Your Trip:

- ❑ Staying at: _______________

  ____

  ____

- ❑ Phone _________________
- ❑ Reservations? ____Y ____N

  for dates ________________

- ❑ Check in time __________
- ❑ Check out time __________
- ❑ Dog friendly _____Y ____N
- ❑ Max RV length ___________
- ❑ Dump Station location

  ____

  ____

- ❑ Distance from home

  miles: _________________

  hours: _________________

JOURNAL THE ADVENTURE

Why I went:

Dates I was in the park:

Where I stayed:

Who I went with:

How I got there: (circle all that apply)

Weather Experienced

Rate the Park

1 2 3 4 5

Will I go again?

Yes Maybe No

Memorable sights and experiences:

Something funny:

Something surprising:

Something disappointing:

One thing I want to remember about this trip:

North & Mid-ATLANTIC REGION

- Maine
- Virginia
- West Virginia

MORE PARKS IN THE ATLANTIC REGION

If you live or are traveling in the Northeast and want to make a bucket list for National Parks in that area, it may seem that you are out of luck. We only have one "official" National Park in the NE so, what can you do?

Use this list and the blank pages at the end of this book to enjoy a trip to some of these areas. See page 85 for the abbreviations key.

Connecticut

- ❑ Weir Farm NHS

Maine

- ❑ Acadia National Park
- ❑ Saint Croix Island International HS

Massachusetts

- ❑ Adams NHP
- ❑ Boston African American NHS
- ❑ Boston Harbor Islands NBA
- ❑ Boston NHP
- ❑ Cape Cod NS
- ❑ Frederica Law Olmstead NHS
- ❑ John Fitzgerald Kennedy NHS
- ❑ Longfellow House- Washington's Headquarters NHS
- ❑ Lowell NHP
- ❑ Minute Man NHP
- ❑ New Bedford Whaling NHP
- ❑ Salem Maritime NHS
- ❑ Sangus Iron Works NHS
- ❑ Springfield Armory NHS

New Hampshire

- ❑ Saint-Gaudens NHS

New York

- ❑ African Burial Ground NM
- ❑ Castle Clinton NM
- ❑ Eleanor Roosevelt NHS
- ❑ Federal Hall N MEM
- ❑ First Island NM
- ❑ Gateway NRA
- ❑ General Grant N MEM
- ❑ Governors Island NM
- ❑ Hamilton Grange N MEM
- ❑ Home of Franklin D Roosevelt NHS
- ❑ Martin Van Buren NHS
- ❑ Sagamore Hill NHS
- ❑ Statue of Liberty NM
- ❑ Theodore Roosevelt Birthplace NHS
- ❑ Theodore Roosevelt Inaugural NHS
- ❑ Vanderbilt Mansion NHS
- ❑ Women's Rights NHP

Rhode Island

- ❑ Roger Williams N MEM

Vermont

- ❑ Marsh-Billings-Rockefeller NHP

ACADIA NATIONAL PARK

State: Maine   Date Est: February 26, 1919

Explore the Park Virtually: https://www.nps.gov/acad/index.htm

Address:
25 Visitor Center Rd,
Bar Harbor,
Hancock ME 04609

Open all year _____Y_____N

dates___________________

- ❑ Phone (207) 288-3338
- ❑ Park Hours ____________
- ❑ Entrance $ ____________
- ❑ Timed Entrance ________
- ❑ Camp Sites $ __________
- ❑ RV Sites $ ____________
- ❑ Refund policy

____

____

By the Numbers:

- ❑ 3.4 million+ visitors per year
- ❑ 49,000+ acres
- ❑ Lat. 44.40897, Long -68.24728
- ❑ 4 park entrances
- ❑ 6 visitor centers
- ❑ Highest elevation 1,528 ft.
- ❑ Lowest elevation 0 ft.

Attractions to Experience:

- ❑ Sieur de Monts Nature Center ❑
- ❑ Wild Gardens of Acadia ❑
- ❑ Carroll Homestead ❑
- ❑ Isleford Historical Museum ❑
- ❑ Stargazing at Jordan Pond ❑
- ❑ Hike Compass Harbor Trail ❑
- ❑ Hike Jesup Path & Hemlock Path Loop ❑ ❑
- ❑ Carriage Road Bridges Tour ❑

Notes

____

____

____

____

____

____

____

____

____

____

____

Plan Your Trip:

- ❑ Staying at: ______________

  ____

  ____

- ❑ Phone ________________
- ❑ Reservations? ____Y ____N

  for dates ______________

- ❑ Check in time __________
- ❑ Check out time _________
- ❑ Dog friendly _____Y ____N
- ❑ Max RV length __________
- ❑ Dump Station location

  ____

  ____

- ❑ Distance from home

  miles: ________________

  hours: ________________

JOURNAL THE ADVENTURE

Why I went:

Dates I was in the park:

Where I stayed:

Who I went with:

How I got there: (circle all that apply)

Weather Experienced

Rate the Park

1 2 3 4 5

Will I go again?

Yes Maybe No

Memorable sights and experiences:

One thing I want to remember about this trip:

Something funny:

Something surprising:

Something disappointing:

SHENANDOAH NATIONAL PARK

State: Virginia Date Est: December 26, 1935

Explore the Park Virtually: https://www.nps.gov/shen/index.htm

Address:
Thornton Gap Entrance
3655 US-211,
Luray, VA 22835

Open all year _____Y_____N

dates____________________

- ❑ Phone (540) 999-3500
- ❑ Park Hours ____________
- ❑ Entrance $ ____________
- ❑ Timed Entrance ________
- ❑ Camp Sites $ __________
- ❑ RV Sites $ ____________
- ❑ Refund policy

____

____

By the Numbers:

- ❑ 1.4 million+ visitors per year
- ❑ 199,000+ acres
- ❑ Lat. 38. 66241,
  Long -78.32081
- ❑ 4 park entrances
- ❑ 2 visitor centers
- ❑ Highest elevation 4,050 ft.
- ❑ Lowest elevation 561 ft.

Attractions to Experience:

- ❑ Dicky Ridge VC
- ❑ Harry F Byrd VC
- ❑ Massanutten Lodge
- ❑ Rapidan Camp Tour
- ❑ Big Meadows Area
- ❑ Stargazing / Int'l Dark Sky Park
- ❑ Fox Hollow Trail Tour
- ❑ Appalachian Trail – Tanners Ridge Road

- ❑
- ❑
- ❑
- ❑
- ❑
- ❑
- ❑
- ❑
- ❑

Notes

____

____

____

____

____

____

____

____

____

____

____

Plan Your Trip:

- ❑ Staying at: ______________

  ____

  ____

- ❑ Phone ________________
- ❑ Reservations? ____Y ____N

  for dates ______________

- ❑ Check in time ___________
- ❑ Check out time __________
- ❑ Dog friendly _____Y ____N
- ❑ Max RV length ___________
- ❑ Dump Station location

  ____

  ____

- ❑ Distance from home

  miles: _________________

  hours: _________________

JOURNAL THE ADVENTURE

Why I went:

Dates I was in the park:

Where I stayed:

Who I went with:

How I got there: (circle all that apply)

Weather Experienced

Rate the Park

1 2 3 4 5

Will I go again?

Yes Maybe No

Memorable sights and experiences:

Something funny:

Something surprising:

Something disappointing:

One thing I want to remember about this trip:

NEW RIVER GORGE NATIONAL PARK

State: West Virginia — Date Est: December 21, 2020

Explore the Park Virtually: https://www.nps.gov/neri/index.htm

Address:
New River Gorge Bridge,
Fayetteville, WV 25840

- ❑ Phone (304) 574-2115
- ❑ Park Hours ____________
- ❑ Entrance $ ____________
- ❑ Timed Entrance ________
- ❑ Camp Sites $ __________
- ❑ RV Sites $ ____________
- ❑ Refund policy
  ____
  ____

Open all year _____Y_____N

dates__________________

By the Numbers:

- ❑ _________ visitors per year
- ❑ 7,000+ acres
- ❑ Lat. 38.06996,
  Long -81.076
- ❑ 4 park entrances
- ❑ 4 visitor centers
- ❑ Highest elevation 3,291 ft.
- ❑ Lowest elevation 240 ft.

Attractions to Experience:

- ❑ Drive Fayette Station Scenic Rd
- ❑ Fish for smallmouth bass
- ❑ Take the African American Heritage Driving Tour
- ❑ Snap a pic at Grandview
- ❑ Visit Thurmond Historic Dist.
- ❑ Visit Sandstone Falls
- ❑ Nuttallburg Historic Mining Town
- ❑
- ❑
- ❑
- ❑
- ❑
- ❑
- ❑
- ❑
- ❑

Plan Your Trip:

- ❑ Staying at: _______________
  ____
  ____
- ❑ Phone ________________
- ❑ Reservations? ____Y ____N
  for dates ________________
- ❑ Check in time ___________
- ❑ Check out time __________
- ❑ Dog friendly _____Y ____N
- ❑ Max RV length ___________
- ❑ Dump Station location
  ____
  ____
- ❑ Distance from home
  miles: _________________
  hours: _________________

Notes

____
____
____
____
____
____
____
____
____
____
____

JOURNAL THE ADVENTURE

Why I went:

Dates I was in the park:

Where I stayed:

Who I went with:

How I got there: (circle all that apply)

Weather Experienced

Rate the Park

1 2 3 4 5

Will I go again?

Yes Maybe No

Memorable sights and experiences:

Something funny:

Something surprising:

Something disappointing:

One thing I want to remember about this trip:

Do You Know The NPS Digital App?

There is one app to give you access to every park – right at your fingertips.

The NPS App is the new official app for the National Park Service with tools to explore more than 400 national park properties throughout the USA.

You'll find interactive maps, ideas for tours to take in each park (if available), up to date information about accessibility due to weather and COVID-19, and much more.

Looking for something to do? Search the app by park name or for "parks near me." You can see which properties are in your state, and even search by topic – from African American Heritage to Women's History.

Each individual park in the app has :

- ❑ A photo gallery
- ❑ Information about fees
- ❑ What to see
- ❑ Where to Stay
- ❑ Tours to experience
- ❑ Visitor center info
- ❑ Hiking trails to explore – with difficulty levels
- ❑ A park calendar
- ❑ And information about where to get your park stamp

The free app is currently available for iOS and Android devices. It's the perfect companion to use as you plan your national park adventures before going there, and then to use during your trip for up to date information about activities.

Don't go to a park without it!

SOUTHEAST REGION

- Florida
- Kentucky
- South Carolina
- Tennessee
- Virgin Islands

BISCAYNE NATIONAL PARK

State: Florida

Date Est: June 28, 1980

Explore the Park Virtually: https://www.nps.gov/bisc/index.htm

Address:
Dante Fascell Visitor Center
9700 SW 328th St,
Homestead, FL, 33033

Open all year _____Y_____N

dates___________________

- ❑ Phone (305) 230-1144
- ❑ Park Hours ____________
- ❑ Entrance $ ____________
- ❑ Timed Entrance _________
- ❑ Camp Sites $ ___________
- ❑ RV Sites $ _____________
- ❑ Refund policy

____

____

By the Numbers:

- ❑ 700,000+ visitors per year
- ❑ 172,000+ acres
- ❑ Lat. 38.06996, Long -81.076
- ❑ 1 park entrance
- ❑ 1 visitor center
- ❑ Highest elevation 10 ft.
- ❑ Lowest elevation 0 ft.

Attractions to Experience:

- ❑ Tour the Maritime Heritage Trail (by boat)
- ❑ Visit Boca Chita Key lighthouse
- ❑ Hike the Elliot Key loop
- ❑ Walk "Spite Highway"
- ❑ Paddle the mangroves
- ❑ Snorkel at a shipwreck
- ❑ Take a kiteboarding lesson
- ❑ Eco-adventure: Jones Lagoon
- ❑
- ❑
- ❑
- ❑
- ❑
- ❑
- ❑
- ❑
- ❑

Notes

____

____

____

____

____

____

____

____

____

____

____

Plan Your Trip:

- ❑ Staying at: ______________

  ____

  ____
- ❑ Phone _________________
- ❑ Reservations? ____Y ____N

  for dates _________________
- ❑ Check in time ___________
- ❑ Check out time __________
- ❑ Dog friendly _____Y ____N
- ❑ Max RV length ___________
- ❑ Dump Station location

  ____

  ____
- ❑ Distance from home

  miles: _________________

  hours: _________________

JOURNAL THE ADVENTURE

Why I went:

Dates I was in the park:

Where I stayed:

Who I went with:

How I got there: (circle all that apply)

Weather Experienced

Rate the Park

1 2 3 4 5

Will I go again?

Yes Maybe No

Memorable sights and experiences:

One thing I want to remember about this trip:

Something funny:

Something surprising:

Something disappointing:

DRY TORTUGAS NATIONAL PARK

State: Florida

Date Est: October 26, 1992

Explore the Park Virtually: https://www.nps.gov/drto/index.htm

Address:
Florida Keys Eco Discovery Center
35 E Quay Rd,
Key West, FL 33040

Open all year _____Y_____N

dates___________________

- ❑ Phone (305) 242-7700
- ❑ Park Hours ____________
- ❑ Entrance $ ____________
- ❑ Timed Entrance _________
- ❑ Camp Sites $ ___________
- ❑ RV Sites $ _____________
- ❑ Refund policy

____

____

By the Numbers:

- ❑ 79,000+ visitors per year
- ❑ 64,000+ acres
- ❑ Lat. 24.6279, Long -82.87265
- ❑ 1 park entrance
- ❑ 2 visitor centers
- ❑ Highest elevation 10 ft.
- ❑ Lowest elevation 0 ft.

Attractions to Experience:

- ❑ Explore North Coaling Dock ruins
- ❑ Visit Garden Key Lighthouse
- ❑ Taka a self- guided tour of Fort Jeffferson
- ❑ Rodman Cannon
- ❑ Snorkel Little Africa
- ❑ Paddle to Loggerhead Key
- ❑ Take a Ranger Guided tour

❑
❑
❑
❑
❑
❑
❑
❑
❑

Notes

____

____

____

____

____

____

____

____

____

____

____

Plan Your Trip:

- ❑ Staying at: _______________

  ____

  ____

- ❑ Phone ________________
- ❑ Reservations? ____Y ____N

  for dates _______________

- ❑ Check in time __________
- ❑ Check out time __________
- ❑ Dog friendly _____Y ____N
- ❑ Max RV length ___________
- ❑ Dump Station location

  ____

  ____

- ❑ Distance from home

  miles: _________________

  hours: _________________

JOURNAL THE ADVENTURE

Why I went:

Dates I was in the park:

Where I stayed:

Who I went with:

How I got there: (circle all that apply)

Weather Experienced

Rate the Park

1 2 3 4 5

Will I go again?

Yes Maybe No

Memorable sights and experiences:

Something funny:

Something surprising:

Something disappointing:

One thing I want to remember about this trip:

EVERGLADES NATIONAL PARK

State: Florida
Date Est: May 30, 1934

Explore the Park Virtually: https://www.nps.gov/ever/index.htm

Address:
Ernest F. Coe Visitor Center
40001 State Hwy 9336,
Homestead, FL 33034

Open all year _____Y_____N

dates___________________

- ❑ Phone (305) 242-7700
- ❑ Park Hours ____________
- ❑ Entrance $ ____________
- ❑ Timed Entrance _________
- ❑ Camp Sites $ ___________
- ❑ RV Sites $ ____________
- ❑ Refund policy

____

____

By the Numbers:

- ❑ 1.1 million+ visitors per year
- ❑ 1.5 million+ acres
- ❑ Lat. 25.39531, Long -80.58307
- ❑ 3 park entrances
- ❑ 4 visitor centers
- ❑ Highest elevation 20 ft.
- ❑ Lowest elevation 0 ft.

Attractions to Experience:

- ❑ Experience Flamingo
- ❑ Hike Snake Bite Trail
- ❑ Paddle Nine Mile Pond
- ❑ Experience Shark Valley
- ❑ Otter Cave Hammock Trail
- ❑ Climb Shark Valley Observation Tower
- ❑ Experience Gulf Coast Sandfly Hiking Trail

- ❑
- ❑
- ❑
- ❑
- ❑
- ❑
- ❑
- ❑
- ❑

Notes

____

____

____

____

____

____

____

____

____

____

____

Plan Your Trip:

- ❑ Staying at: _______________

  ____

  ____

- ❑ Phone ________________
- ❑ Reservations? ____Y ____N

  for dates ________________

- ❑ Check in time ___________
- ❑ Check out time __________
- ❑ Dog friendly _____Y ____N
- ❑ Max RV length ___________
- ❑ Dump Station location

  ____

  ____

- ❑ Distance from home

  miles: _________________

  hours: _________________

JOURNAL THE ADVENTURE

Why I went:

Dates I was in the park:

Where I stayed:

Who I went with:

How I got there: (circle all that apply)

Weather Experienced

Rate the Park

1 2 3 4 5

Will I go again?

Yes Maybe No

Memorable sights and experiences:

One thing I want to remember about this trip:

Something funny:

Something surprising:

Something disappointing:

MAMMOTH CAVE NATIONAL PARK

State: Kentucky

Date Est: July 1, 1941

Explore the Park Virtually: https://www.nps.gov/maca/index.htm

Address:
1 Mammoth Cave Pkwy,
Mammoth Cave, KY 42259

Open all year _____Y_____N

dates___________________

- ❑ Phone (270) 758-2180
- ❑ Park Hours ____________
- ❑ Entrance $ ____________
- ❑ Timed Entrance _________
- ❑ Camp Sites $ ___________
- ❑ RV Sites $ _____________
- ❑ Refund policy

____

____

By the Numbers:

- ❑ 550,000+ visitors per year
- ❑ 54,000+ acres
- ❑ Lat. 37.18698, Long -86.10122
- ❑ 4 park entrances
- ❑ 1 visitor center
- ❑ Highest elevation 852 ft.
- ❑ Lowest elevation 421 ft.

Attractions to Experience:

- ❑ Old Guide's Cemetery ❑
- ❑ Stroll Heritage Trail ❑
- ❑ Walk Sand Cave Trail ❑
- ❑ Walk Sloan's Crossing Pond Tr. ❑
- ❑ Self guided Mammoth Passage ❑ Cave Tour (fee) ❑
- ❑ Choose from one of 6 guided ❑ cave tours (fees apply) ❑
- ❑ Ranger-led stargazing program ❑

Notes

____

____

____

____

____

____

____

____

____

____

____

Plan Your Trip:

- ❑ Staying at: _______________

  ____

  ____
- ❑ Phone _______________
- ❑ Reservations? ____Y ____N

  for dates _______________
- ❑ Check in time ___________
- ❑ Check out time __________
- ❑ Dog friendly _____Y ____N
- ❑ Max RV length ___________
- ❑ Dump Station location

  ____

  ____
- ❑ Distance from home

  miles: _______________

  hours: _______________

JOURNAL THE ADVENTURE

Why I went:

Dates I was in the park:

Where I stayed:

Who I went with:

How I got there: (circle all that apply)

Weather Experienced

Rate the Park

1 2 3 4 5

Will I go again?

Yes Maybe No

Memorable sights and experiences:

Something funny:

Something surprising:

Something disappointing:

One thing I want to remember about this trip:

CONGAREE NATIONAL PARK

State: South Carolina

Date Est: November 10, 2003

Explore the Park Virtually: https://www.nps.gov/cong/index.htm

Address:
100 National Park Rd,
Hopkins, SC 29061

Open all year _____Y_____N

dates___________________

- ❑ Phone (803) 776-4396
- ❑ Park Hours ____________
- ❑ Entrance $ ____________
- ❑ Timed Entrance ________
- ❑ Camp Sites $ __________
- ❑ RV Sites $ ____________
- ❑ Refund policy

____

____

By the Numbers:

- ❑ 159,000+ visitors per year
- ❑ 26,000+ acres
- ❑ Lat. 33.82962, Long -80.82341
- ❑ 1 park entrance
- ❑ 1 visitor center
- ❑ Highest elevation 140 ft.
- ❑ Lowest elevation 80 ft.

Attractions to Experience:

- ❑ Stroll Boardwalk Loop Trail
- ❑ View the pines as you hike Bluff Trail
- ❑ Paddle Cedar Creek Canoe Tr.
- ❑ Take the guided Nature Discovery walk
- ❑ In May/June – catch Synchronous Fireflies
- ❑ Fishing!

- ❑
- ❑
- ❑
- ❑
- ❑
- ❑
- ❑
- ❑
- ❑

Notes

____

____

____

____

____

____

____

____

____

____

____

Plan Your Trip:

- ❑ Staying at: ______________

  ____

  ____

- ❑ Phone _________________
- ❑ Reservations? ____Y ____N

  for dates _______________

- ❑ Check in time __________
- ❑ Check out time __________
- ❑ Dog friendly _____Y ____N
- ❑ Max RV length __________
- ❑ Dump Station location

  ____

  ____

- ❑ Distance from home

  miles: _________________

  hours: _________________

JOURNAL THE ADVENTURE

Why I went:

Dates I was in the park:

Where I stayed:

Who I went with:

How I got there: (circle all that apply)

Weather Experienced

Rate the Park

1 2 3 4 5

Will I go again?

Yes Maybe No

Memorable sights and experiences:

One thing I want to remember about this trip:

Something funny:

Something surprising:

Something disappointing:

GREAT SMOKY MOUNTAINS N. P.

State: Tennessee / N Carolina — Date Est: June 15, 1934

Explore the Park Virtually: https://www.nps.gov/grsm/index.htm

Address:
Sugarlands VC
1420 Fighting Creek Gap Rd,
Gatlinburg, TN 37738

- ❑ Phone (865) 436-1200
- ❑ Park Hours ____________
- ❑ Entrance $ ____________
- ❑ Timed Entrance __________
- ❑ Camp Sites $ ___________
- ❑ RV Sites $ ____________
- ❑ Refund policy

____

____

Open all year _____Y_____N

dates___________________

By the Numbers:

- ❑ 12 million+ visitors per year
- ❑ 522,000+ acres
- ❑ Lat. 33.82962, Long -80.82341
- ❑ 6 park entrances
- ❑ 4 visitor centers
- ❑ Highest elevation 6,643 ft.
- ❑ Lowest elevation 5,046 ft.

Attractions to Experience:

- ❑ Take an auto tour on Cades Cove Loop Rd
- ❑ Visit a historic cemetery
- ❑ Hike to Alum Cave
- ❑ Visit Newfound Gap
- ❑ Snap a pic of Clingmans Dome
- ❑ Hike Abrams Falls Trail
- ❑ Grotto Falls Trail waterfall
- ❑ Climb Chimney Tops for views

❑
❑
❑
❑
❑
❑
❑
❑
❑

Notes

____

____

____

____

____

____

____

____

____

____

____

Plan Your Trip:

- ❑ Staying at: _______________

  ____

  ____

- ❑ Phone _________________
- ❑ Reservations? ____Y ____N

  for dates ________________

- ❑ Check in time ___________
- ❑ Check out time __________
- ❑ Dog friendly _____Y ____N
- ❑ Max RV length ___________
- ❑ Dump Station location

  ____

  ____

- ❑ Distance from home

  miles: ________________

  hours: ________________

JOURNAL THE ADVENTURE

Why I went:

Dates I was in the park:

Where I stayed:

Who I went with:

How I got there: (circle all that apply)

Weather Experienced

Rate the Park

1 2 3 4 5

Will I go again?

Yes Maybe No

Memorable sights and experiences:

Something funny:

Something surprising:

Something disappointing:

One thing I want to remember about this trip:

VIRGIN ISLANDS NATIONAL PARK

State: Virgin Islands

Date Est: August 2, 1956

Explore the Park Virtually: https://www.nps.gov/viis/index.htm

Address:
Virgin Island National Park,
St John 00830, USVI

Open all year _____Y_____N

dates___________________

- ❑ Phone (340) 776-6201 x238
- ❑ Park Hours _____________
- ❑ Entrance $ _____________
- ❑ Timed Entrance _________
- ❑ Camp Sites $ ___________
- ❑ RV Sites $ _____________
- ❑ Refund policy

____

____

By the Numbers:

- ❑ 133,000+ visitors per year
- ❑ 15,000+ acres
- ❑ Lat. 18.33269, Long -64.79378
- ❑ many park entrances
- ❑ 1 visitor center
- ❑ Highest elevation 1,277 ft.
- ❑ Lowest elevation 0 ft.

Attractions to Experience:

- ❑ Visit Trunk Bay Beaches
- ❑ Cinnamon Bay Nature Loop
- ❑ Annaburg Sugar Plantation
- ❑ Guided Birdwatching tour
- ❑ Windmill self-guided tour
- ❑ Snorkel Maho Bay
- ❑ Trunk Bay underwater snorkel trail
- ❑ Stroll Salt Pond Bay trail

- ❑
- ❑
- ❑
- ❑
- ❑
- ❑
- ❑
- ❑
- ❑

Notes

____

____

____

____

____

____

____

____

____

____

____

Plan Your Trip:

- ❑ Staying at: _______________

  ____

  ____

- ❑ Phone _________________
- ❑ Reservations? ____Y ____N

  for dates _______________

- ❑ Check in time __________
- ❑ Check out time __________
- ❑ Dog friendly _____Y ____N
- ❑ Max RV length __________
- ❑ Dump Station location

  ____

  ____

- ❑ Distance from home

  miles: _________________

  hours: _________________

JOURNAL THE ADVENTURE

Why I went:

Dates I was in the park:

Where I stayed:

Who I went with:

How I got there: (circle all that apply)

Weather Experienced

Rate the Park

1 2 3 4 5

Will I go again?

Yes Maybe No

Memorable sights and experiences:

Something funny:

Something surprising:

Something disappointing:

One thing I want to remember about this trip:

PARK:

State: Date Est:

Explore the Park Virtually:

Address:

Open all year _____Y_____N

dates___________________

- ❑ Phone _______________
- ❑ Park Hours _____________
- ❑ Entrance $ _____________
- ❑ Timed Entrance _________
- ❑ Camp Sites $ ___________
- ❑ RV Sites $ _____________
- ❑ Refund policy

____

____

By the Numbers:

- ❑ __________visitors per year
- ❑ __________________acres
- ❑ Lat. __________________,
  Long. __________________
- ❑ ___________ park entrance
- ❑ ___________ visitor centers
- ❑ Highest elevation_______ ft
- ❑ Lowest elevation _______ ft

Attractions to Experience:

❑	❑
❑	❑
❑	❑
❑	❑
❑	❑
❑	❑
❑	❑
❑	❑
❑	❑

Notes

____

____

____

____

____

____

____

____

____

____

____

Plan Your Trip:

- ❑ Staying at: _______________

  ____

  ____
- ❑ Phone _________________
- ❑ Reservations? ____Y ____N

  for dates _______________
- ❑ Check in time ___________
- ❑ Check out time __________
- ❑ Dog friendly _____Y ____N
- ❑ Max RV length ___________
- ❑ Dump Station location

  ____

  ____
- ❑ Distance from home

  miles: _________________

  hours: _________________

JOURNAL THE ADVENTURE

Why I went:

Dates I was in the park:

Where I stayed:

Who I went with:

How I got there: (circle all that apply)

Weather Experienced

Rate the Park

1 2 3 4 5

Will I go again?

Yes Maybe No

Memorable sights and experiences:

One thing I want to remember about this trip:

Something funny:

Something surprising:

Something disappointing:

PARK:

State: Date Est:

Explore the Park Virtually:

Address:

Open all year _____Y_____N

dates____________________

- ❑ Phone _______________
- ❑ Park Hours _____________
- ❑ Entrance $ _____________
- ❑ Timed Entrance __________
- ❑ Camp Sites $ ___________
- ❑ RV Sites $ ____________
- ❑ Refund policy

____

____

By the Numbers:

- ❑ __________visitors per year
- ❑ __________________acres
- ❑ Lat. __________________,
  Long. __________________
- ❑ ___________ park entrance
- ❑ ___________ visitor centers
- ❑ Highest elevation_______ ft
- ❑ Lowest elevation _______ ft

Attractions to Experience:

- ❑
- ❑
- ❑
- ❑
- ❑
- ❑
- ❑
- ❑
- ❑

- ❑
- ❑
- ❑
- ❑
- ❑
- ❑
- ❑
- ❑
- ❑

Notes

____

____

____

____

____

____

____

____

____

____

____

Plan Your Trip:

- ❑ Staying at: _______________

  ____

  ____

- ❑ Phone _________________
- ❑ Reservations? ____Y ____N

  for dates ________________

- ❑ Check in time ___________
- ❑ Check out time __________
- ❑ Dog friendly _____Y ____N
- ❑ Max RV length ___________
- ❑ Dump Station location

  ____

  ____

- ❑ Distance from home

  miles: _________________

  hours: _________________

JOURNAL THE ADVENTURE

Why I went:

Dates I was in the park:

Where I stayed:

Who I went with:

How I got there: (circle all that apply)

Weather Experienced

Rate the Park

1 2 3 4 5

Will I go again?

Yes Maybe No

Memorable sights and experiences:

Something funny:

Something surprising:

Something disappointing:

One thing I want to remember about this trip:

PARK:

State: Date Est:

Explore the Park Virtually:

Address:

Open all year _____Y_____N

dates___________________

- ❑ Phone _______________
- ❑ Park Hours _____________
- ❑ Entrance $ _____________
- ❑ Timed Entrance _________
- ❑ Camp Sites $ ___________
- ❑ RV Sites $ _____________
- ❑ Refund policy

____

____

By the Numbers:

- ❑ __________visitors per year
- ❑ __________________acres
- ❑ Lat. ___________________,
  Long. ___________________
- ❑ ___________ park entrance
- ❑ ___________ visitor centers
- ❑ Highest elevation_______ ft
- ❑ Lowest elevation _______ ft

Attractions to Experience:

- ❑
- ❑
- ❑
- ❑
- ❑
- ❑
- ❑
- ❑
- ❑
- ❑
- ❑
- ❑
- ❑
- ❑
- ❑
- ❑
- ❑
- ❑

Plan Your Trip:

- ❑ Staying at: _______________
  ____
  ____
- ❑ Phone _________________
- ❑ Reservations? ____Y ____N
  for dates ________________
- ❑ Check in time ___________
- ❑ Check out time __________
- ❑ Dog friendly _____Y ____N
- ❑ Max RV length ___________
- ❑ Dump Station location
  ____
  ____
- ❑ Distance from home
  miles: _________________
  hours: ________________

Notes

____

____

____

____

____

____

____

____

____

____

____

JOURNAL THE ADVENTURE

Why I went:

Dates I was in the park:

Where I stayed:

Who I went with:

How I got there: (circle all that apply)

Weather Experienced

Rate the Park

1 2 3 4 5

Will I go again?

Yes Maybe No

Memorable sights and experiences:

Something funny:

Something surprising:

Something disappointing:

One thing I want to remember about this trip:

PARK:

State: Date Est:

Explore the Park Virtually:

Address:

Open all year _____Y_____N

dates____________________

- ❑ Phone _______________
- ❑ Park Hours _____________
- ❑ Entrance $ _____________
- ❑ Timed Entrance _________
- ❑ Camp Sites $ ___________
- ❑ RV Sites $ _____________
- ❑ Refund policy

____

____

By the Numbers:

- ❑ __________visitors per year
- ❑ ___________________acres
- ❑ Lat. ___________________,
  Long. ___________________
- ❑ ___________ park entrance
- ❑ ___________ visitor centers
- ❑ Highest elevation_______ ft
- ❑ Lowest elevation _______ ft

Attractions to Experience:

- ❑
- ❑
- ❑
- ❑
- ❑
- ❑
- ❑
- ❑
- ❑
- ❑
- ❑
- ❑
- ❑
- ❑
- ❑
- ❑
- ❑
- ❑

Notes

____

____

____

____

____

____

____

____

____

____

____

Plan Your Trip:

- ❑ Staying at: _______________

  ____

  ____
- ❑ Phone __________________
- ❑ Reservations? ____Y ____N

  for dates ________________
- ❑ Check in time __________
- ❑ Check out time __________
- ❑ Dog friendly _____Y ____N
- ❑ Max RV length ___________
- ❑ Dump Station location

  ____

  ____
- ❑ Distance from home

  miles: __________________

  hours: _________________

JOURNAL THE ADVENTURE

Why I went:

Dates I was in the park:

Where I stayed:

Who I went with:

How I got there: (circle all that apply)

Weather Experienced

Rate the Park

1 2 3 4 5

Will I go again?

Yes Maybe No

Memorable sights and experiences:

One thing I want to remember about this trip:

Something funny:

Something surprising:

Something disappointing:

PARK:

State: Date Est:

Explore the Park Virtually:

Address:

Open all year _____Y_____N

dates____________________

- ❑ Phone ________________
- ❑ Park Hours ____________
- ❑ Entrance $ ____________
- ❑ Timed Entrance _________
- ❑ Camp Sites $ ___________
- ❑ RV Sites $ _____________
- ❑ Refund policy

____

____

By the Numbers:

- ❑ __________visitors per year
- ❑ ___________________acres
- ❑ Lat. ____________________,
  Long. ____________________
- ❑ ____________ park entrance
- ❑ ____________ visitor centers
- ❑ Highest elevation_______ ft
- ❑ Lowest elevation _______ ft

Attractions to Experience:

❑	❑
❑	❑
❑	❑
❑	❑
❑	❑
❑	❑
❑	❑
❑	❑
❑	❑

Notes

____

____

____

____

____

____

____

____

____

____

____

Plan Your Trip:

- ❑ Staying at: _______________
  ____
  ____
- ❑ Phone _________________
- ❑ Reservations? ____Y ____N
  for dates _______________
- ❑ Check in time __________
- ❑ Check out time __________
- ❑ Dog friendly _____Y ____N
- ❑ Max RV length ___________
- ❑ Dump Station location
  ____
  ____
- ❑ Distance from home
  miles: _________________
  hours: _________________

JOURNAL THE ADVENTURE

Why I went:

Dates I was in the park:

Where I stayed:

Who I went with:

How I got there: (circle all that apply)

Weather Experienced

Rate the Park

1 2 3 4 5

Will I go again?

Yes Maybe No

Memorable sights and experiences:

One thing I want to remember about this trip:

Something funny:

Something surprising:

Something disappointing:

INDEX

- ❑ Acadia National Park 122
- ❑ Arches National Park 106
- ❑ Badlands National Park 102
- ❑ Big Bend National Park 72
- ❑ Biscayne National Park 130
- ❑ Black Canyon of the Gunnison NP 90
- ❑ Bryce Canyon National Park 108
- ❑ Canyonlands National Park 110
- ❑ Capitol Reef National Park 112
- ❑ Carlsbad Caverns National Park 68
- ❑ Channel Islands National Park 40
- ❑ Congaree National Park 138
- ❑ Crater Lake National Park 22
- ❑ Cuyahoga Valley National Park 86
- ❑ Death Valley National Park 42
- ❑ Denali National Park 6
- ❑ Dry Tortugas National Park 132
- ❑ Everglades National Park 134
- ❑ Gates of the Arctic National Park 8
- ❑ Gateway Arch National Park 84
- ❑ Glacier National Park 98
- ❑ Glacier Bay National Park 10
- ❑ Grand Canyon National Park 34
- ❑ Grand Teton National Park 116
- ❑ Great Basin National Park 62
- ❑ Great Sand Dunes NP and Preserve ... 92
- ❑ Great Smoky Mountains NP................. 140
- ❑ Guadalupe Mountains National Park .. 74
- ❑ Haleakala National Park 58
- ❑ Hawaii Volcanoes National Park 60
- ❑ Hot Springs National Park 66
- ❑ Indiana Dunes National Park 78
- ❑ Isle Royale National Park 80
- ❑ Joshua Tree National Park 44
- ❑ Katmai National Park and Preserve 12
- ❑ Kenai Fjords National Park 14
- ❑ Kings Canyon National Park 46
- ❑ Kobuk Valley National Park 16
- ❑ Lake Clark National Park 18
- ❑ Lassen Volcanic National Park 48
- ❑ Mammoth Cave National Park 136
- ❑ Mesa Verde National Park 94
- ❑ Mount Rainier National Park 24
- ❑ National Park of American Samoa 32
- ❑ New River Gorge National Park 126
- ❑ North Cascades National Park 26
- ❑ Olympic National Park 28
- ❑ Petrified Forest National Park 36
- ❑ Pinnacles National Park 50
- ❑ Redwood National Park 52
- ❑ Rocky Mountain National Park 96
- ❑ Saguaro National Park 38
- ❑ Sequoia National Park 54
- ❑ Shenandoah National Park 124
- ❑ Theodore Roosevelt National Park 100
- ❑ Virgin Islands National Park 142
- ❑ Voyageurs National Park 82
- ❑ White Sands National Park 70
- ❑ Wind Cave National Park 104
- ❑ Wrangell | St. Elias NP and Preserve ... 20
- ❑ Yellowstone National Park 118
- ❑ Yosemite National Park 56
- ❑ Zion National Park 114

- ❑ 10 Things to Take & Do On Your National Park Trip 30
- ❑ National Park Trivia 64
- ❑ Types of Parks 76
- ❑ National Parks with Lodges 88
- ❑ More Parks in the Atlantic Region 121